KITCHEN & BATH LIGHTING...
made easy

Michael De Luca, CKD, ASID, NCIDQ Certified

Published by The National Kitchen & Bath Association

BOOK STORE

- **Publisher: Nick Geragi, CKD, CBD, NCIDQ**

- **Director of Communications: Donna M. Luzzo**

- **Director of Marketing: Nora DePalma**

- **Chief Executive Officer: Robert O. Hirsch, Ph.D., CAE**

The National Kitchen & Bath Association, the leading international organization exclusively serving those individuals involved in providing kitchen and bathroom design and remodeling services, is dedicated to researching and publishing information on all facets of the kitchen and bathroom industry. NKBA® will continue to pursue timely subjects that affect the industry and those working in it.

ISBN 1887127-06-2

Information about this book and other NKBA® publications, membership and educational seminars may be obtained from the National Kitchen & Bath Association, 687 Willow Grove Street, Hackettstown, NJ 07840, phone (800) -THE-NKBA, fax (908)-852-1695. e-mail, educate@nkba.org. Visit our website at www.nkba.org.

This book is intended for professional use by kitchen & bath design professionals. The procedures and advice contained herein or in the **LightCalc®** Software program, have been shown to be appropriate for applications described, however, no warranty (expressed or implied) is intended or given by NKBA®, Michael De Luca and Associates, or Enviro-Systems. Moreover, the user of this book is cautioned to be familiar with design and lighting principles.

Other Contributors:

- Content Editor: Nick Geragi, CKD, CBD, NCIDQ, Director of Education and Product Development

- Electronic Publishing and Design: Graphic Image, Inc.

- Cover Kitchen Design by: Kathleen Kennedy, CKD

From the Publisher

Dear Industry Professional,

Together with lighting designer Michael De Luca, NKBA® has created a one-of-a-kind lighting design tool for kitchen and bath designers. Presented in an easily understood format, the author takes you through a simple step-by-step planning process. To round out the design considerations, hard to find technical information on lamping and luminaires from several manufacturers are provided.

Allowing you to create effective lighting schemes for your clients, Michael incorporates information on; color, spacing, light reflectance, fixtures and more. Lighting concepts however, can be complex and intimidating. The secret to understanding the information in this book is to read it the first time, from front-to-back. This will allow you to grasp each lighting concept. Each chapter builds sequentially on the information presented. By the time you have completed the book, you will have a solid understanding of how to calculate your lighting plans.

The book is filled with practical applications too. So in addition to referring to the lamping specifications in the appendices, *Kitchen & Bath Lighting ... made easy*, will become a resource you'll be using again and again.

Nick Geragi, CKD, CBD, NCIDQ
Publisher, NKBA Books
Director of Education and Product Development

TABLE OF CONTENTS

Lamps & Fixtures .... Chapter 5

Practical Application .... **Chapter 6**

INTRODUCTION

I have met and talked with many interior designers and kitchen and bath designers over the years at local workshops, national shows, and focus groups. Whenever the subject turns to lighting, almost every designer I have talked with reacts by doing two things. First, they show immediate enthusiasm about the subject and secondly, a dark cloud seems to envelop them as they remember their frustration over past lighting experiences. It is truly amazing to watch. In their attempts to learn the fundamentals of lighting, what continues to thwart them is how information on lighting is presented; either too technically, too generally, or too "rule-of-thumbish."

The goal of this book is to present information in a conversational style based on practical field experience. The most common complaint about books dealing with these issues is that they are too dry, making the process of getting through them almost Herculean. A little sugar has always helped the medicine go down. In this case, the medicine is the technical lighting concepts, the formulas, etc., presented in the sugar of a little levity and playfulness. The end result is that you will end up with more technical knowledge than headache and with a valuable tool you can use in your design practice everyday... and maybe you'll have a good time doing it.

Why We Are Confused

Two types of lighting information exist on the bookshelves today: technical manuals written by engineers and lighting design books written by designers. Both address important issues. The engineering based tomes explore every nuance of light energy, how it is created, how it is measured, how it is affected by everything from reflectance to, it seems, the alignment of the planets. They offer superhuman mathematical equations to quantify it all, too. Unfortunately, most designers do not hold a master's degree in math and just can't understand it! Engineers write for other engineers, not for designers.

Don't get me wrong. Engineers are like gods to me. How they ever conceive ways to measure and quantify physical phenomena amazes me. Their ability to analyze what we cannot see, or what we take for granted, finds its way into our lives as products like the integrated chip (which makes computer technology possible) or halogen or compact fluorescent lamps. It is just when they define something like a lumen as, "the unit of luminous flux equal to the flux in a unit solid angle of one steradian from a uniform point source of one candlepower," that I get frustrated.

In this book, I will tell you that a lumen is, "the intensity or quantity of light energy produced by any lamp." Engineers will look condescendingly on my definition, but which do you understand? True, my definition is not technically complete, but it describes all that you must know to incorporate the concept of lumens into the foundation of knowledge we are seeking to build here. In addition, since most designers are right brain dominant (creative), they tend to learn by the written word with more difficulty than if the same information is presented visually. Toward this end, I will "paint" visual pictures, and offer analogies and graphic interpretations of technical concepts that the designer will comprehend more readily... but will cause a lighting engineer to convulse.

Let's move on to lighting design books written by designers. This genre of books deals with the aesthetic qualities lighting brings to a project rather than how to determine which of the thousands of available lamps is the right one to use. These important aesthetic qualities are the perceptions of reality we have or the illusion of reality designers are trained to create. I have gained valuable insights from these books, and recommend them, but have always been left without the skill to determine which lamps to choose and how far apart to space them. Sure, there are formulas in the books, but no explanations on how or when to implement them.

This book will introduce you to the Inverse Square Law and the Lumen Method, two different methods for determining how to choose the proper lamp for a space. You will also be shown how to space the lamps properly to get the effect you, the designer, desire.

Before we move on, I would like to caution you about "rule-of-thumb" solutions. THEY DON'T WORK! There are books out there that actually tell designers to select the quantity of lamps for a space by allotting "x" number of watts per square foot of floor space in the room. **This does not work.** Depending on the lamp design, fewer watts in one lamp can produce more actual illumination than another lamp of a higher wattage. And what about spacing the lamps? It depends on the cone of light the lamp or lamp/fixture is producing. It has nothing to do with watts. For example, spacing will be different when using a spot versus a flood and will change again from an 8 foot to a 10 foot ceiling height. And what about color? A dark room will need twice as many lamps, or lamps twice as powerful as a light colored room. Of course, there are a few "rules-of-the-road" that are safe to use because the results can be counted on in virtually all situations. These are included throughout the book.

In this book I have endeavored to reduce the necessary math to a minimum. That which is required is relatively easy to do.

I have also collaborated on a software program, **LightCalc**®, that does all the math for you, instantly telling you which lamp to use for the various rooms and activities in the home. **LightCalc**® presents a dynamically changing cross section of the lamp's cone of light so you can see the area a lamp covers. The program also recommends proper lamp spacing regardless of the ceiling height.

The Goals Of This Book

In this book, you will acquire an excellent foundation of lighting knowledge and the ability to discern when, where, and how to apply it.

Here is what you will learn:

- **How colors used in a room affect the quantity of light required**

- **How the color of a lamp affects the color of objects in the room**

- **How to determine the appropriate footcandle level for any room in the home**

- **How to calculate the quantity and intensity of lamps needed in a space**

- **How to choose the appropriate incandescent or fluorescent lamp**

- **Advantages of halogen lighting**

- **Advantages of fluorescent lighting**

- **How to determine appropriate lamp spacing**

- **How to differentiate between general and task lighting**

- **How to find and utilize information published in manufacturers' specifications**

- **How to differentiate between fluorescent lamp types and why cool or warm white lamps shouldn't be used in a designed space**

- **How to select and locate art lighting so it will actually hit the art**

- **When to use recessed, surface, or track lighting**

- **How to create a lighting plan for a kitchen and a bath incorporating general and task lighting**

Beyond the benefits you may reap, the book is also written for the benefit of the clients who use our services. They deserve the best we can provide. After all, who else is responsible for the opportunity we enjoy in practicing our craft? The astute designer will understand this simple point of service.

Who Should Read This Book

You should read this book if you have been frustrated by the types of information available on lighting, yet are truly interested in providing good lighting for your design projects. The information and insights will prove valuable to those new to the field of lighting design, as well as the experienced designer, or anyone who does not enjoy figuring out a lighting plan amid twenty binders strewn about the office. This book was written to replace the twenty with only one. Toward this end, Lamp Data Tables have been included in the appendices from General Electric, Phillips, and Sylvania/Osram. The only thing you should need beyond this book are the fixture specifications. See the "Resources" listing in the back of the book for fixture and lamp manufacturers along with their phone numbers and addresses.

How To Use This Book

Start with Chapter 1, *Lighting Concepts.*

Do the exercises at the end of the chapter!

Read the glossary.

Work your way through the remaining chapters doing the exercises at the end of chapters 2 through 4. These will help you retain the information.

Familiarize yourself with the information in the various appendices, especially the spacing and candlepower tables. These are invaluable time saving tools for lighting designers of every experience level.

When you see an insert like this:

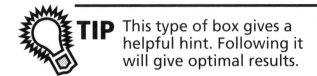

TIP This type of box gives a helpful hint. Following it will give optimal results.

it contains helpful information and "rules-of-the-road" which can make it a little easier to put into practice the information you will learn in this book, not to mention make your lighting designs better.

When you see an insert like this:

This type of box warns against doing something really bad.

it means be careful! Ignoring the advice contained within it may lead to disastrous results.

When you encounter a graphic, make sure to read it carefully. I would not have taken the time to create it if it were not important in getting a point across.

It is my sincere hope that you find the information contained in these pages useful, easy to understand, and a real tool for implementing good lighting design. It is to you and your clients that I dedicate this book.

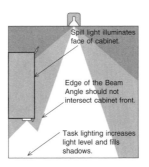

Spill light illuminates face of cabinet.

Edge of the Beam Angle should not intersect cabinet front.

Task lighting increases light level and fills shadows.

CHAPTER 1

LIGHTING CONCEPTS

The following concepts are fundamental to building a foundation of lighting knowledge and are used in explanations throughout this book:

- **General Lighting**
- **Task Lighting**
- **Workplane**
- **Distance**
- **Footcandle**
- **Lumen**
- **Candlepower**
- **Watts**
- **Lamp Data Tables**

Once you are comfortable with the information contained in this chapter, go on to the glossary. Only then, unless you have previous lighting experience, should you proceed with the rest of the book.

General Lighting

Every room must have enough illumination to navigate through it and to do general, nonspecific activities appropriate to it. The amount of illumination required for the space will vary according to the usual activities of the room. The Illumination Engineering Society (IES) has set standards concerning these lighting levels which are expressed in footcandles, a unit of measurement for defining the amount of illumination on a surface.

In any given room, the lighting designer must calculate the footcandle level for the workplane, the height above the floor at which most work occurs. When there is no specific workplane height (counter, table, desk, etc.), such as in a living room, the amount of light will be calculated for an assumed workplane height of 2 1/2 feet above the floor.

 **TIP** General lighting for usual activities

- Should illuminate the entire space evenly.
- Is calculated for the workplane height.

 **TIP** Task lighting for specific activities

- Should illuminate work areas.
- Is calculated for the workplane height.

When determining general lighting, the goal is to provide the space with an illumination level evenly distributed throughout the room. Think of the great outdoors. When you step outside, the lighting level is even, whether it is partly cloudy, sunny, dawn or dusk. This is how general lighting should be approached. To do this, the fixture spacing must be accurately determined based on the lamp's cone of light and the distance the lamp is from the workplane. Lamp spacing is the topic of Chapter 3, *Spacing Principles.*

A question often comes up in lighting discussions about the kitchen, "My client doesn't want to spend the additional money for under-cabinet lighting. Can't I just move the recessed can lights closer to the wall cabinets to provide counter and overall lighting with the same lamp?" **The answer is no.**

As you will learn in Chapter 4, *Lighting Measurements,* one lamp mounted in a recessed can at a specific distance from the counter cannot provide both general and task lighting levels at the same time.

Task Lighting

Specific tasks are often associated with a given room, such as working at the sink in a kitchen, or reading at a desk in an office or study. These tasks require more visual acuity and a higher level of illumination than general lighting. They are performed at a specific height above the floor, known as the workplane, which is measured in feet above the floor for lighting calculations. Task lighting is in addition to, not instead of, the general illumination for the room. Eye strain is most often caused by inadequate lighting.

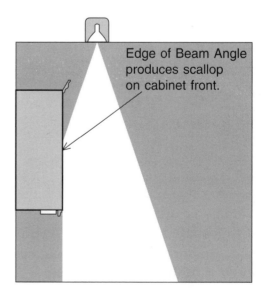

Edge of Beam Angle produces scallop on cabinet front.

Figure 1.1   ***Beam angle intersecting cabinet face***

By moving the lamps closer to the wall cabinets, the cone of light produced by the lamp is cut by the face of the cabinets, producing a nasty scallop on the front of wall cabinets. This scallop rarely aligns with the symmetry of the doors, causing visual confusion as it affects shadow, line, rhythm, etc. Try to avoid this.

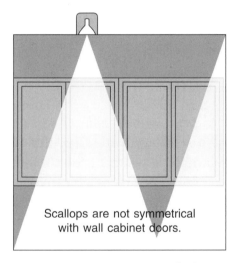

Scallops are not symmetrical with wall cabinet doors.

Figure 1.2   Scallops out of phase

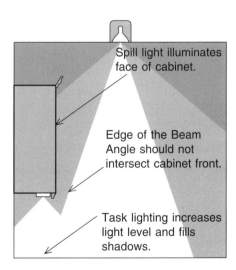

Spill light illuminates face of cabinet.

Edge of the Beam Angle should not intersect cabinet front.

Task lighting increases light level and fills shadows.

Figure 1.3   Shows the best relationship between general & task fixture positions

The best solution is to use one light source for general lighting and another for task lighting. In this way, the general lighting fixtures can be moved away from the cabinet fronts while the task fixtures illuminate the workplane to a higher level for activity that is more visually intensive.

These issues are further discussed in Chapter 3, *Spacing Principles.*

 All work counter areas for the kitchen, bath, laundry, etc., are considered task surfaces and must be illuminated to a higher level than the surrounding general lighting.

Workplane

In any space the workplane is the actual or implied surface upon which an activity takes place. It is this surface that must have a specific level of light to perform a task comfortably. The more visually difficult the task, the greater the level of light must be. In order to determine the amount of light a lamp is providing to this horizontal plane cutting through the room, it is necessary to determine its height above the floor measured in feet.

 **TIP** The workplane is a horizontal plane through the space where most of the work occurs.

Footcandle levels are measured on this surface.

For a kitchen, the countertop is the workplane typically at 3 feet above the floor. The bath can be anywhere from 2 1/2 to 3 feet above the floor. A dining room or desk workplane is 2 1/2 feet high. When there is not a specific surface upon which an activity will take place, such as in a family or living room, a 2 1/2 foot workplane height is assumed. Whether you are calculating general or task illumination, the light level is determined in footcandles measured at the workplane height.

Distance

Distance is simply the measurement, in feet, between the lamp and the workplane.

TIP Distance is the measurement between the workplane and the lamp, in feet.

It is used in the Inverse Square Law and Lumen Method.

In a kitchen with a ceiling height of 8 feet and a workplane at 3 feet, the distance to the workplane will be 5 feet (8 feet minus 3 feet = 5 feet). For recessed cans or high hats, use the ceiling height to determine the distance.

As you work through this book, it will become abundantly clear that as a lamp moves away from the workplane, the light level on the workplane is reduced. As it gets closer, the level increases.

Distance is a **critical** part of lighting calculations.

Footcandle

The Footcandle is a unit of measurement that describes the amount of light on a surface, workplane, art, etc.

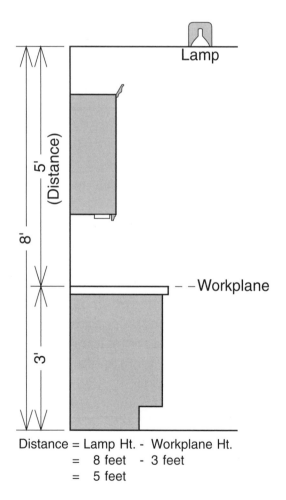

Lamp

Workplane

Distance = Lamp Ht. - Workplane Ht.
= 8 feet - 3 feet
= 5 feet

Figure 1.4   ***Workplane & distance***

Chapter 1 — Lighting Concepts

TIP Footcandle is a workplane measurement.

- It measures illumination level on the workplane.

- It is used in the Inverse Square Law & Lumen Method.

- Recommended levels defined by the IES.

- See Chapter 4, *Lighting Measurements,* for details.

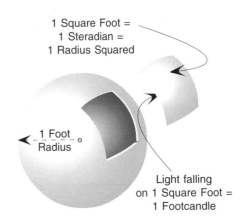

1 Square Foot =
1 Steradian =
1 Radius Squared

1 Foot
Radius

Light falling
on 1 Square Foot =
1 Footcandle

Figure 1.5   *Footcandle*

Every room has a specific general lighting and often a task lighting footcandle level as recommended by the IES. The goal in lighting design is to find the lamp that will produce the appropriate footcandle level on the workplane. See Chapter 4, *Lighting Measurements* for information on how to determine recommended footcandle levels for a specific room or task.

The following description of what determines the unit of measurement known as the footcandle is not important to remember. However, there are those among us who love technical minutia. Some use it to impress potential clients with their competence. A well placed bit of technical trivia delivered in the client-designer interview has gotten me a job or two. If you are so inclined, read on. The rest of you, by all means, can move on to the next topic.

If a candle were suspended in mid-air, its wick lit, and the wax candle part removed, we would have an omni-directional light source in space. If a sphere with a one foot radius were wrapped around the flame, the result would be an orb two feet in diameter with a candle flame illuminating its entire interior surface equally. If we isolate a curved section of the sphere with an area equal to the radius squared (one square foot) and measure the light directly on its surface, it is equal to one footcandle.

There are exactly 12.57 of these one radius square, curved planes in any sphere. They are known as steradians.

Lux - for European Lamps

European lighting manufacturers provide lighting measurements in lux. When using European fixtures such as Hera, Hettich, Hafele, etc., it is important to be able to convert their lux measurements to footcandles. Proceed with any of the calculations found in Chapter 4, *Lighting*

Measurements, which use footcandles, then convert to lux prior to selecting your European lamps or fixtures.

Just like converting between inches and centimeters, converting between footcandles and lux is achieved by multiplying either one by a factor:

 **TIP**

$$\text{Lux} = \text{FC} \times 10.76$$
$$\text{FC} = \text{Lux} \times .0929$$

The metric version of the footcandle, lux, is the same except the radius of the sphere is one meter. The light measured on one square meter, then, is equal to one lux. Since the sphere is larger, the steradian is larger, but there are still only 12.57 of them.

Lumen

There are two ways to measure the intensity or volume of light a lamp produces. They are the lumen and candlepower. *All* light sources have an inherent lumen measurement but not all have a candlepower rating.

 **TIP**

Lumen is a lamp measurement.

It measures the omni-directional quantity or intensity of ALL lamps.

It is used in the Lumen Method.

It is determined by the lamp manufacturer.

See Appendix A, *Lamp Specifications,* for details.

The lumen is a unit of measurement defining the quantity of light a lamp produces; its intensity or raw power. The Lumen Method calculation uses lumen quantities to calculate the number of fixtures required in a room to produce the desired footcandle level and how far apart to space them. See Chapter 4, *Lighting Measurements,* for a description of the Lumen Method.

Understand that the lumen is a measurement of the *lamp* and **not** of the illumination it produces on the workplane. We must know how powerful the lamp is, and how far it is away from the workplane, to calculate the footcandle level it produces on the workplane.

Candlepower

Like lumens, candlepower is a measurement of the lamp's intensity, but only if the lamp is directional (narrow spot, spot, flood, wide flood, etc.).

 **TIP**

Candlepower is a lamp measurement.

It measures the focused quantity or intensity of directional lamps.

It is used in the Inverse Square Law.

It is determined by the lamp manufacturer.

See Appendix A, *Lamp Specifications,* for details.

If you look in the Lamp Data Tables in Appendix A, you will note that the only time candlepower is given is when a beam angle is defined (indicating a directional lamp). There will never be a candlepower rating for omni-directional lamps (fluorescent, A type, etc.). Note that **all** lamps have a lumen quantity. However, some manufacturers opt not to list it.

To distinguish the difference between lumen and candlepower, we must paint an engineer-defying visual analogy. Under-stand that we can measure the quantity or intensity of light emanating from the sun in lumens and that the sun is omni-directional. Since the sun is omni-directional, it will have no candlepower measurement.

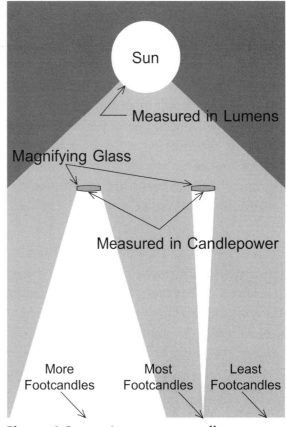

Figure 1.6   *Lumen vs. candlepower*

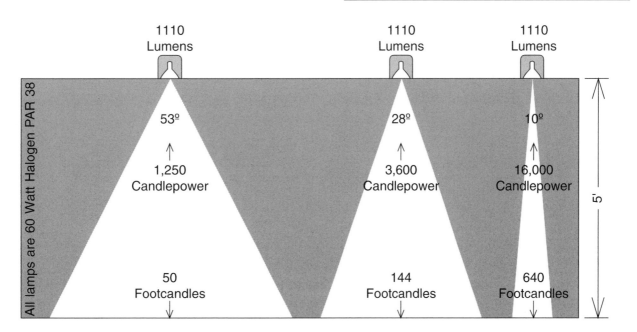

Figure 1.7   *Lamps of the same lumen output will have varied candlepower output according to the beam angle.*

If we take an ordinary magnifying glass and position it so that we concentrate the light energy of the sun into a focused beam of light, the newly concentrated light energy can now be measured in candle-power. It is at the lens of the magnifying glass that the candlepower measurement is taken. By repositioning the glass to focus the light more tightly into a pinpoint, there will be enough concentrated energy and heat to ignite a flame.

In essence, this is what goes on inside a directional lamp. The filament produces a quantity of light (measured in lumens) and the design of the lamp redirects or focuses the light into a defined cone of light (measured in candlepower).

Candlepower is used in the Inverse Square Law while lumens are used in the Lumen Method. Why do we need both types of measurements? Not all information is provided by the manufacturers of lamps and fixtures. We can use different calculation methods for determining the proper lamp and spacing depending on the type of information available. Chapter 4, *Lighting Measurements*, discusses in detail when to use lumens versus candlepower. For now, it is sufficient to know that they measure different aspects of the lamp's light energy.

Getting back to the sun and the magnifying glass example, it becomes clear that the sun, with only a single lumen value, can have several candlepower intensities simply by readjusting the magnifying glass. This is

also true of directional lamps. In figure 1.7, three lamps are shown of the same type, 60 watt PAR 38, all at 1110 lumens positioned at 5 feet off the workplane. One is a spot, one a flood, and one a wide flood. Notice as the beam narrows, the candlepower rises and so does the footcandle level. This relationship between lumens, candlepower, distance, and footcandles is fundamental and unchanging. Make sure you are clear on it before moving on. Much of the up-coming material will find its basis here.

TIP Lamp data charts some-times express candle-power as candelas. They are interchangeable.

Beam Angle

A directional lamp focuses or redirects its light energy into a cone emanating from the lamp's lens where it is measured in candle-power. The center of the cone has the most intense light, while the edges have the least. It has been determined that at certain intervals a perceptible drop in the illumina-tion occurs across the cone.

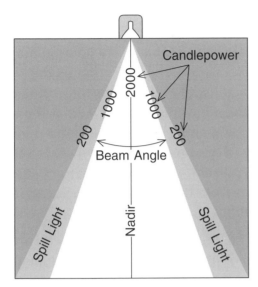

The Beam Angle is defined where Candlepower falls to 50%.

Figure 1.8   ***Beam angle & spill light***

If a lamp is measured at the center of the cone (nadir) at 2000 footcandles, for example, the first notable drop in illumination occurs where the candlepower falls to 50% or 1000 candlepower. This establishes what is known as the beam angle. The beam angle is what is used in spacing directional lamps to provide a uniform field of light in a room or for a specific task area. The beam angle is found in the lamp manufacturers' Lamp Data Table.

Although the beam angle ranges from 100%, center-beam candlepower (2000 in our example), to 50% (1000 in our example), the candlepower for the entire beam angle is considered to be its center-beam candlepower for use in lighting calculations.

Beyond the beam angle the light continues to drop and, at 10% (200 candlepower in our example), the next noticeable change occurs. The area outside the beam angle, from 50% to 10% of the lamp's center-beam candlepower, is known as spill light. Spill light is obviously less bright than the beam angle and is not considered in spacing. It is, however, adequate for providing a *fudge* zone when ideal spacing can't be achieved due to ceiling joists, duct work, etc. Spill light does provide adequate illumination of wall cabinet fronts without producing an unpleasant scallop.

Scallops are produced by allowing a vertical surface to intersect the beam angle.

Directional lamps produce their own beam angle while omni-directional lamps rely on the fixture and trim to redirect the light energy, forming an implied beam angle. In other words, an omni-directional lamp alone cannot achieve a cone of light. It is the assembly (lamp, fixture, and trim) working in concert that forms the equivalent of a beam angle.

For directional lamp spacing, either the Lumen Method can be used or a geometric section can be constructed using the lamp's beam angle. For omni-directional lamps, the Lumen Method must be used to determine fixture spacing. See Chapter 3, *Spacing Principles.*

Watts

Wattage tells how much electricity the lamp will burn. **Wattage tells nothing about the amount of light a lamp can produce**. The wattage listed on lamps of a similar type can, however, allow some comparison. For example, when comparing two R40 Flood lamps (one 75 watts and the other 100 watts) from the same manufacturer, it is reasonable to assume that the 75-watt lamp is less powerful than the 100-watt lamp.

However, it is entirely possible for a lamp from a different class to be lower in wattage, yet provide more light; a 60-watt PAR 38 lamp, for instance, will have approximately three times the candlepower when compared to the aforementioned 75-watt R40 lamp.

It is my theory that the number one reason for rooms being under-illuminated is that lamps are chosen by price, and watts saved, rather than by proper lumen or candlepower at the lowest wattage available.

Lamp Data Tables

Lamp Data Tables from lighting manufacturers are the specification guides for the characteristics of the lamps they produce. You must have one to know what the lamps are doing and to do the calculations in this book. Fortunately, we have included the most current, at press time, Lamp Data Tables from the major manufacturers in *Appendix A*.

The information printed directly on the lamp or its package never shows lumens, beam angle, or candlepower. I know this doesn't make any sense, but how much sense does it make for one cabinet manufacturer to call a sink base a BS36 while another calls it a SB36 or a BSC36? It is just the way it is... for now.

For directional lamps, both lumens and candlepower will be listed in *Appendix A*. For omni-directional lamps, only lumens will be listed when available. Whether the color rendition index, color temperature, lamp life, or efficiency of the lamp, etc. will be listed, depends on the manufacturer. See Chapter 2, *Color & Reflectance*, and the *Glossary* for more information on these terms.

QUIZ

1. What two types of lighting should be planned for most every room?

   _____   _____

2. General lighting requires more illumination than task lighting?

   T   F

3. Task lighting is calculated at the work plane height. General lighting is calculated at the _____?

   a.) Floor
   b.) Workplane

4. At what height should the general illumination be calculated in a living or family room?

   _____

5. Distance is the measurement between the _____ and the _____?

6. If pendants are to be used over an island in a kitchen with an 8-foot ceiling and the pendant lamp is 1 1/2 feet below the ceiling, what is the distance?

   _____

7. The quantity or intensity of light energy emanating from *any* lamp can be measured in _____?

8. Candlepower measures the intensity or quantity of light energy for which type of lamp?

   a.) Fluorescent
   b.) Directional
   c.) Halogen
   d.) All of the above

9. Lumen is a measurement at the _____?

10. Candlepower is a measurement at the _____?

11. Footcandles are measured on the _____?

12. Which calculation method uses lumens?

    _____

13. Which calculation method uses footcandles, distance, and candlepower?

    _____

14. As the focus of a lamp (the beam angle) narrows, candlepower will?

   a.) Increase
   b.) Decrease
   c.) Remain unchanged

15. In question 14, the footcandle level will?

   a.) Increase
   b.) Decrease
   c.) Remain unchanged

16. The beam angle is that portion of the cone of light which ranges from 100% to 50% of the lamp's measured candlepower?

   T   F

17. The width of the beam angle is used in?

   a.) Determining footcandles
   b.) Spacing lamps to provide even illumination
   c.) Geometry

18. Watts are used to determine the amount of light a lamp can produce?

   T   F

19. Where can crucial specifications such as candlepower, beam angle, lumens, etc. be found in order to perform lighting calculations?

   _____

20. Candlepower and candela are sometimes used synonymously by lamp manufacturers?

   T   F

   See *Solutions* in the back of the book for answers and explanations.

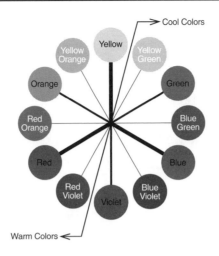

CHAPTER 2

COLOR & REFLECTANCE

Light and Color

Light is our perception of the energy radiating from a light source. It may come directly to the eye or be reflected from some other object.

Color, then, is our perception of the various wave lengths of light we see as hue (yellow, blue, red, etc.) through the interaction of the light source and the reflector. There is no perception of color without light. Light radiating from a lamp also has an inherent color which influences our perception of colored objects illuminated by it.

Light strikes colored objects and is reflected back into the space. Depending on the color of the objects reflecting the light, the overall illumination level can change dramatically.

Fundamentally, there can be no discussion of light without a basic understanding of how color affects lighting and of how lighting affects color. In the following topics:

- **Color Rendition Index**
- **Color Temperature**
- **Reflectance**

we will discuss the quality and quantity of lighting in any room as affected by the colors used in the room, inherent lamp color, and a lamps ability to render color accurately.

Color Rendition Index

The Color Rendition Index (CRI) is a scale from 1 to 100 which describes the effectiveness of a light source in reproducing accurately, an object's color, 100 being the best.

 **TIP** Whenever possible, use lamps with a CRI over 80 for best results.

If we think in evolutionary terms, our eyes were designed to perceive the colors of an object when illuminated by the sun. The sun has a CRI index of 100. All incandescent lamps, halogen or otherwise, will have a CRI of over 98. As the index falls off the 100 mark, color shifting occurs affecting our perception of what the objects true colors are. The best lamps to use are those with a CRI rating over 80. Since all incandescent lamps have a CRI over 98, CRI is not a concern for them. However, fluorescent lamps are quite another issue.

 **TIP** All residential incandescent lamps have a CRI of 98 - 100.

We all grew up with Warm White (WW) and Cool White (CW) lamps manufactured in four foot tubes. While these lamps are quite energy efficient and produce negligible heat, they have CRI ratings of 50 and 60 respectively. This is well below the acceptable level of 80. Color corrected fluorescent lamps are now available in 70, 80, and (with rare earth phosphors) 90 CRI.

Comparing Fluorescent Lamps

This is a good time to discuss the difference in fluorescent lamps as it relates to overall cost and to what is being returned in terms of color quality and number of lamps required.

 **TIP** Fluorescent lamps are available in 50, 60, 70, 80, and 90 CRI.

Utility fluorescent lamps, Cool White (CW) and Warm White (WW), with 50-60 CRI have poor color rendering properties, yet yield a high lumen output. For years the economy of these lamps, though lacking good color rendering technology, have justified their use. Today, however, technology advancements have provided some alternatives.

Moving up in quality, one step above CW and WW, to a lamp that provides approximately 70 CRI, we find that the lumen output improves. Illuminating a space using these lamps will provide better color accuracy, and it will take fewer lamps to do it. Note that the CRI is still below the recommended 80. Taking into consideration that the lamps are more expensive to start with, some economy is gained.

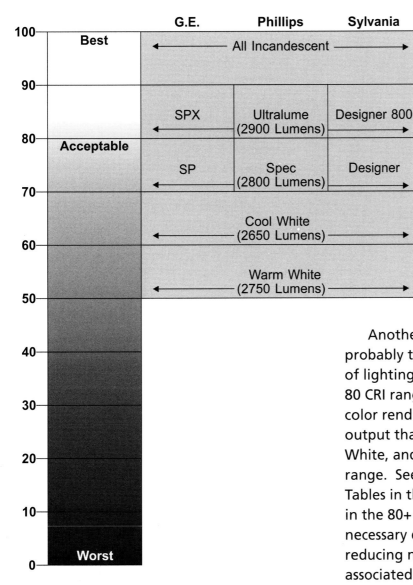

Figure 2.1 **Color Rendition Index**

Another step up in caliber will provide probably the best balance between quality of lighting and economy. Using lamps in the 80 CRI range will produce a very acceptable color rendition and yield a higher lumen output than either Cool White or Warm White, and higher than lamps in the 70 CRI range. See the Fluorescent Lamp Data Tables in the Appendices. By selecting lamps in the 80+ CRI range, fewer lamps will be necessary due to the higher lumen output reducing not only energy costs, but the associated electricians' costs as well. Fluorescent lamps in the 80 CRI range will be less expensive in the long run and are the preferred choice.

While the Color Rendition Index is not perfect, it does offer the best gauge for designers of any residential interior space to use. However, an understanding of both color rendition and color temperature is necessary to select an appropriate lamp.

Color Temperature

Understand that color rendition is not the only factor affecting color that must be considered when choosing an appropriate lamp for a space. The effect of a lamp's color temperature also changes our perception of colors used in the room.

Color temperature describes how the lamp itself appears when illuminated. Color temperature is measured in Kelvin ranging from over 10,000k (which appears blue) down to 1,000k (which appears orange-red). Light sources used for general lighting fall somewhere in between, with color temperatures ranging from high (3,600k - 5,500k) considered "cool"; neutral (3,000k - 3,600k), and low (2,700k - 3,000k) considered "warm."

An analogy may help to remember that a higher color temperature represents itself as a "cooler" color and vice versa. Picture a candle flame. The base of the flame where the temperature is the highest is blue in color. Blue, however, is a "cool" color. Conversely, at the tip of the flame, the temperature is lower and its color, yellow. Yellow is a "warm" color.

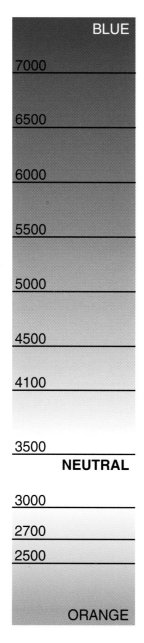

 **TIP** Color temperatures:

Cool	3,600k-5,500k
Neutral	3,000k-3,600k
Warm	2,700k-3,000k

The color wheel can be divided in half; the colors on one side are considered cool and those on the other are perceived as warm.

Figure 2.2   ***Color temperature range***

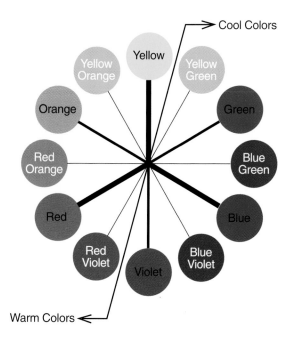

Figure 2.3 **Warm & cool on the wheel**

Many factors affect the appearance of an object's color: the finishes used on surrounding walls, floors, furnishings; the intensity level of the lighting, and the presence of daylight in the room. All of these factors should be considered in selecting the appropriate light source.

Often the color palette used in a room will fall into either predominately warm or cool. To illustrate how color temperature affects the colors in a room it is important to understand a little about color and what happens when a color is mixed with its complement.

A complementary color, or hue, is that color directly across the color wheel from another (i.e., orange is the complement of blue and blue is the complement of orange.) When orange is mixed with blue in equal amounts, gray is the result. When lesser amounts of orange are mixed with blue, a washed out or "grayed" out blue results.

Much like mixing a color with its complement, using cool, blue light will wash out warmer colors. Using cool light will intensify cool colors. Using warm or yellow-orange light will intensify warm colors and wash out cool colors. Lamps that are neutral in color will not affect either warm or cool colors. Which effect is correct?

The "right" choice is something no one will ever agree on. Some experts say to use cool lamps (color temperature 3,600k - 5,500k) with predominately cool colors, neutral lamps (3,000k - 3,600k) with a neutral scheme, and warm lamps (2,700k - 3,000k) with predominately warm colors.

 **TIP** Use lamps between 2,900k - 3,600k for most general & task lighting.

In my experience, there is seldom a color scheme that is devoid of either warm or cool colors. Using warm or cool lamps will always intensify one while negating the other. In addition, since lighting is intended for the user or viewer of the room, and since people are warm colored objects and are often viewed as well, and since people like to be seen at their best, it seems that there would never be a reason to use cool lamps for general or task lighting. Instead, in selecting lamps tending toward the warmer side of neutral (2,900k - 3,200k), neither warm nor cool colors will be affected adversely, neutral colors will remain neutral, and people in the room will not look like they should be appearing in 'Night Of The Living Dead.' In other words, a *good* thing.

There are times when, for effect, cool or warm lamps can be the best choice. Knowing how color temperature affects an objects color can help in "fixing" a white that is a little too blue or a little too pink.

Regardless of the intended use, color temperature is extremely important and should be the first criterion for lamp selection.

A Little About Lamps

Incandescent lamps are typically on the "warm" side. Halogen lamps (a type of incandescent) are on the "warm" side of neutral ...Hmmm. Fluorescent lamps are available, in the better qualities, in a variety of color temperatures. As an example, G.E.'s *SPX* series lamps come in 3,000k, 3,500k, and 4,100k.

Some clients mistakenly think that a fluorescent labeled *Daylight* should be a wonderful lamp. The logic runs something like this: daylight comes from the sun, the sun is good, so a *Daylight* lamp must also be good. In checking the manufacturer's Lamp Data Table, you will find the color temperature of a *Daylight* lamp is 6,500k; one of the *coolest* (most blue) residential lamps available.

 **TIP** In a room, lamps should appear to be the same color temperature.

One thing to remember: always use lamps of the same color temperature in any room. It doesn't matter if fluorescent is combined with incandescent as long as they are the same color temperature. If the color temperature of lamps used in a room varies, similarly colored objects will appear to vary in color as well.

An important note should be made here. People perceive color differently. I find that a 3,000k halogen lamp appears to be the same color as a 3,500k fluorescent. Consequently, when using fluorescent for the general lighting and halogen for task and accent lighting, I will use the 3,500k fluorescent to keep colors looking consistant.

 Dimming a lamp will cause it to look warmer.

Using a dimmer will lower the lamp's color temperature causing it to look warmer. Think of a flashlight with a weak battery; the lamp becomes amber in color. This is why it is so important to calculate the footcandle level accurately. Dimming a lamp is acceptable and can achieve a nice effect, but don't utilize the dimmer to correct for a lamp that is too powerful for the space.

Reflectance

Reflectance is the amount of light which reflects off an object. This quantity of light can be measured and is expressed as footlamberts. It isn't terribly important for the interior designer to know the technical definition of footlamberts. It is important, however, to understand that the amount of light reflected off objects in a room adds to the overall illumination and must be taken into account when determining the foot-candle requirement for the space. The color of an object determines to a large extent the amount of light reflecting off the object. See Chapter 4, *Lighting Measurements* for more information.

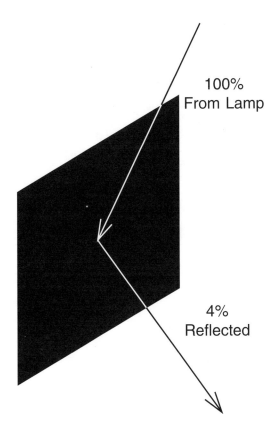

Figure 2.4   **Reflected light from a black surface**

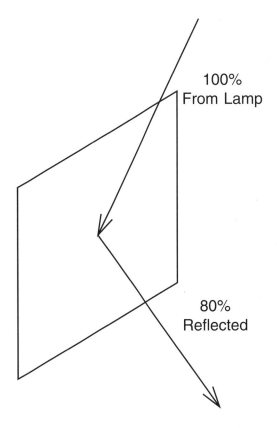

Figure 2.5   **Reflected light from a white surface**

As you can see in figure 2.4, only 4% of the light hitting a black painted wall reflects back into the room.

When the same light hits a white surface, 80% of the light is reflected back into the room (see figure 2.5.)

In most cases there are a variety of materials and colors in a space and the combined reflectance is what must be considered when determining the footcandle level necessary for any room or task. This is because the reflected light adds to the overall illumination, beyond that directly emanating from the lamp. Therefore, a room with all white surfaces (reflecting 80 % of the light back into the room) will require fewer lamps to maintain a given footcandle level. A room with all black surfaces (reflecting 4% of the light back into the room) will depend solely on the light from the light source, thus requiring more lamps to maintain the same level of light.

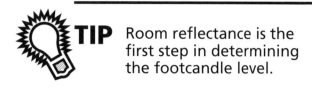
TIP Room reflectance is the first step in determining the footcandle level.

To determine the reflectance of a surface in a room, it is necessary to correlate it to a color or material from the following table. If an exact match is not found in the table, find the closest alternative and use it. In the case of a patterned, multi-colored material (such as wallpaper), approximate the "blended" color of the pattern and match that. An easy way to do this is to let your eyes lose focus while looking at the pattern.

It is necessary to separate the room into the three following areas and determine, for each, an average reflectance.

- **Ceiling Reflectance**   (CR)
- **Wall Reflectance**   (WR)
- **Floor Reflectance**   (FR)

Reflectance Table

Colors	%	Materials	%
White	70-80	Mirror	95
Light cream	70-80	Plaster	80
Light yellow	55-65	White enamel	65-75
		Glazed white tiles	60-75
Light green	45-50		
Pink	45-50	Maple *(Natural)*	60
Sky-blue	40-45	Birch *(Natural)*	60
Light gray	40-45	Light oak	40
		Dark oak	15-20
Beige	25-35	Dark walnut	15-20
Yellow ocher	25-35		
Light brown	25-35	Concrete	15-40
Olive green	25-35	Red brick	5-25
Orange	20-25		
Vermilion red	20-25	Carbon-black	2-10
Medium gray	20-25		
		Clear glass	6-8
Dark green	10-15		
Dark blue	10-15	Ideal Ceilings	60-90
Dark red	10-15	Ideal Walls	35-60
Dark gray	10-15	Ideal Countertops	30-50

Table 2.6   ***Reflectance of various colors & materials***

To illustrate how this can be done in a kitchen, let's assume a 10 foot x 10 foot room with a ceiling height at 8 feet. The ceiling color is white, about 50% of the walls have natural maple cabinetry, windows and doors comprise about 20% of the wall surfaces, and the balance is a deep green wallpaper. The floor is a warm gray slate. The counters are white. There are a variety of materials in this room; some you will determine by color and others by an associated material in the reflectance table, figure 2.6.

Ceiling Reflectance

Most ceilings are white or off white. Looking at the table, white has a reflectance of 70% to 80%; go ahead and use 80% for the white ceiling.

Wall Reflectance

Determining the average reflectance for the walls is a little more difficult. Divide the room into the most prevalent materials, but limit it to three or you will go nuts. For example, in our sample kitchen the walls would be comprised of windows and wall openings, cabinetry, and wallpapered areas.

The next step is to unfold the four walls of the room and determine the overall square footage. The room has four walls, 10 feet x 8 feet totalling 80 square feet each. Multiply the 80 square feet by the four walls to get the total wall surface of 320 square feet.

Assign each of the three types of materials a percentage of wall space:

Cabinetry = 50%
160 square feet

Windows/Openings = 20%
64 square feet

Wallpaper = 30%
96 square feet

Now assign each material a reflectance level from the table:

Natural Maple = 60%

Windows/Openings = 4%

Dark Green = 15%

Note that clear glass has a reflectance of 6% to 8% and that a hole (an opening in a wall) would let all light pass through it and would reflect nothing. The average of the two would roughly be 4%.

Finally, we must reduce the above information into a combined reflectance level for all four walls. Complete the following procedure:

Multiply the square footage percentage for each material by its reflectance.

Cabinetry   **(.50 x .60) = .30**

Windows/Openings (.20 x .04) = .008

Wallpaper   **(.30 x .15) = .045**

                        Total = .353

The average wall reflectance for our little kitchen is 35%.

Floor Reflectance

The floor is determined in the same way as the ceiling. Our sample kitchen's warm gray slate floor is still waiting and, in looking at the reflectance table, the closest would be the medium gray at 25%.

Final Reflectance Tasks

Later, in determining the footcandle level, it will be necessary to provide two additional pieces of information.

- **Average Room Reflectance**
- **Background Reflectance**

Average Room Reflectance

We now have a value for all three of the reflectance cavities in the room:

Ceiling	**=**	**80%**
Walls	**=**	**35%**
Floor	**=**	**25%**

We can average these percentages by totalling them and dividing by their number.

$$= \frac{.80 + .35 + .25}{3}$$

$$= \frac{1.40}{3}$$

$$= .47$$

The average room reflectance is 47%.

Background Reflectance

There is also a consideration for the color, and its reflectance, directly behind the task at hand. The white color of the page you are looking at is the background to the black letters. The background reflectance, then, for this page is 80% as is the background reflectance for the white countertop in our kitchen example. Note that background reflectance is not part of average room reflectance. It will be considered separately when determining the footcandle level.

The background reflectance is 80%.

A Parting Thought on Reflectance

As you will see later, the calculations for reflectance are not as critical as they may appear here. Basically, the objective is to determine whether the overall room is dark (less than 30% reflectance), medium (30% to 70%), or light (more than 70%); about the accuracy of toast. The average room reflectance for the sample kitchen is 47% which is considered medium reflectance.

While the reflectance does profoundly affect the footcandle requirement, don't kill yourself breaking down every subtle nuance of color in the space. It is sufficient to get only a light, medium, or dark general reflectance level. This will make more sense later in Chapter 4, *Lighting Measurements*, as it deals with the influence reflectance has on determining footcandle levels.

QUIZ

1. CRI is an index which indicates a lamp's ability to?
   a.) shed light on a subject.
   b.) create a defined beam angle.
   c.) render the colors of an object accurately.

2. CRI is based on an index from 1 - 100 in which perfect color rendering is considered 100.
   T   F

3. For interior design purposes, it is best to select a lamp capable of at least?
   a.) 60 CRI
   b.) 70 CRI
   c.) 80 CRI

4. In selecting the quality of fluorescent lamps, the most expensive lamps are the best choice because?
   a.) they produce the highest lumen output which means fewer lamps will be needed. Fewer lamps mean lower electrical costs.
   b.) they are over 80 CRI.
   c.) in the long run, they actually cost less than the least expensive lamps.
   d.) they last many more hours than the CW or WW.
   e.) All of the above.

5. When planning on using incandescent lamps, it is important to check the manufacturer's specifications to determine the CRI since it can vary greatly.
   T   F

6. All halogen lamps are incandescent, but all incandescent lamps are not halogen.
   T   F

7. Lamps in the 2,700k - 3,000k color temperature range are considered?
   a.) "Cool" which intensifies "warm" colors, causes neutral colors to appear blue, and negates "cool" colors.
   b.) Directional
   c.) "Warm" which intensifies "warm" colors, causes neutral colors to appear pink, and negates "cool" colors.

8. Lamps ranging from the "warm" side of neutral (2,900k to 3,600k) are generally considered the best choice for most situations.
   T   F

9. Most halogen lamps range from
   a.) 2,700k - 3,000k.
   b.) 2,900k - 3,200k.
   c.) 3,000k - 3,600k.

10. Most incandescent lamps are "warm" in color.

    T   F

11. Better quality fluorescent lamps are available in a wide variety of color temperatures.

    T   F

12. If the lamp CRI is over 80, color temperature need not be considered.

    T   F

13. With regard to color temperature, it is best to avoid mixing incandescent and fluorescent lamps in the same room.

    T   F

14. Light reflecting off objects in the room
    a.) adds to the overall illumination in the space.
    b.) varies depending on the color of the objects.
    c.) must be taken into account when determining the footcandle level for a space.
    d.) All of the above.

15. Colors on the color wheel are considered either "warm" or "cool."

    T   F

16. What is the *estimated* reflectance of a rich mahogany-colored cherry cabinet?

    _____%

17. What is the overall reflectance of a kitchen with an off-white ceiling, wall surface materials by percentage of coverage at 50%, medium stained maple cabinetry; 25% medium green floral wall paper; 25% openings and windows, a rust counter material, and an ecru floor?

    Ceiling Reflectance   _____%

Cabinetry	.50	x _____	=	_____%
Wall Covering	.25	x _____	=	_____%
Openings	.25	x _____	=	_____%
Wall Reflectance				_____%

    Floor Reflectance   _____%

    Overall Reflectance   _____%

18. In question 17, what is the background reflectance of the counter?

    Counter Reflectance   _____%

19. When the colors of a room are not known when doing a lighting plan, it is best to assume the room will be
    a.) Light
    b.) Medium
    c.) Dark

20. The goal of considering reflectance in a room is to determine whether the room is overall light, medium, or dark as a prelude to calculating the footcandle level for the space.

    T   F

See *Solutions* in the back of the book for answers and explanations.

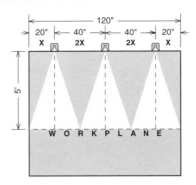

CHAPTER 3

SPACING PRINCIPLES

The layout of the light fixtures on the ceiling is all important in creating an even field of illumination throughout an area and to make sure the lighting covers the intended surface or object. A properly organized ceiling is also pleasing to the eye, providing greater visual harmony which gives the feeling of more volume in the room. Once the spacing interval between fixtures is decided upon, it can be divided into the room, both length and width, to determine the total number of fixtures needed. Task lighting, whether provided by recessed or pendant fixtures, will follow the same layout rules.

In Chapter 1, *Lighting Concepts*, the beam angle was introduced. Remember that some lamps produce their own beam angle

(measured like any other angle in degrees) while others rely on the fixture and trim to redirect the light out of the fixture and into the room. Lamps that produce their own cone of light are said to be directional and the rest are omni-directional. It is necessary to be able to set the spacing for both types of lamps.

This chapter will discuss spacing techniques for:

- **Directional Lamps**
  - General lighting
  - Task lighting

- **Omni-Directional Lamps**
  - General lighting

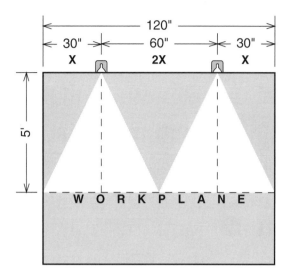

Figure 3.1   *Two cones of light*

Cones Are Everything

The first thing to understand about spacing is that light from a luminaire, whether using a directional or omni-directional lamp, will produce a cone of light which ultimately rests on the workplane. In elevation, the cone appears as a triangle, while in plan view it appears as a circle on the workplane surface. It is the relationship of one triangle to another and one circle to another that spacing is all about.

If the cones of light do not meet as they rest upon the workplane, Figure 3.1, there will be a "gap" of light in between or a dark area. If the cones overlap, the result will be a bright spot. The bright spot occurs because light is additive. If two lamps are placed side by side (no space in between) the light under the pair will be double that under one lamp. So the trick in even illumination is not to have any bright or dark spots between cones. This brings us back to triangles. By looking at the triangular sections of cones across an area we can see

just where the overlap occurs based on the beam angle of the lamp, the distance of the lamp from the surface, and the spacing between lamps.

Triangles

Forget about beam angles for now and take a look at Figure 3.1. Just consider the triangles of light produced by the two lamps in this 120 inch wide area. Notice that the cones have been divided in half, that there are two half cones between lamps, and only one at each end. This is crucial to distributing evenly the light throughout the area or across a task surface whether using recessed or pendant lighting.

 **TIP** Always think of spacing in terms of evenly distributed half cones.

Each half cone has been represented by an "x". If you add all the "x"s (in this case 4) and divide the total into the room width, you will discover the value for "x" is 30 inches. At the ends of the room, where there is only one half cone, the spacing from the wall to the first lamp is 30 inches and where there are two "x"s (two half cones) between lamps, the spacing is 60 inches.

 **TIP** Spacing between lamps should be twice that at the ends.

Equally dividing the Spacing from wall to wall will cause bright spots. See Fig. 3.2.

Avoid the common mistake of making the space between lamps equal to that between the lamp and the wall. This actually causes the lighting to be uneven due to the much greater overlap of half cones between pairs compared to no overlap at the ends.

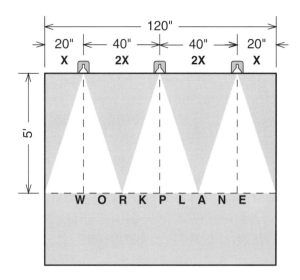

Figure 3.3   Three cones of light

However, at some point the ceiling will take on a decidedly Swiss cheese effect. For general lighting, try to keep the spacing somewhere between 48 inches to 72 inches. This does not apply to task or accent fixture placement.

**TIP** Maintain 48" - 72" spacing for general lighting.

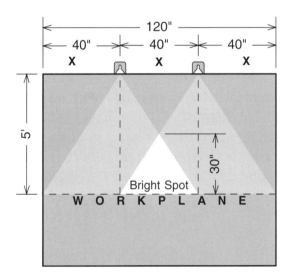

Figure 3.2   Improper spacing

What about when there are more than two lamps? Figure 3.3 shows the same room with three lamps. Notice again that there is one half cone at each end and two half cones between each pair of lamps. Count the "x"s (6) and divide the total into 120 inches. This time "x" equals 20 inches and becomes the spacing from the wall to the first lamp, with 40 inches between lamps. No matter how many lamps are used across an area, this relationship will remain true.

That may have seemed too easy. Well... you're right. Spacing the lamps as we just did does not take into account the beam angle. It is fairly obvious that the cones in Figure 3.1 are much wider than those in Figure 3.3. The next phase of spacing, then, is to find the beam angle that fits the spacing you would like (if you are that lucky) or the spacing you are stuck with due to existing ceiling joist placement or a skylight opening, etc. The next section in this chapter explains how to do just that.

Spacing for General Lighting Using Directional Lamps

Figures 3.4 through 3.12 describe the process of determining the spacing for general lighting using a protractor to construct the cones of light produced by directional lamps. The diagrams give a very good visual representation of how the cones of light relate to one another through an area and how to avoid harsh scallops on a wall or on the wall cabinet fronts.

The Spacing Table, Figure 3.15, provides a faster way to establish spacing. By working through the step-by-step descriptions of the following diagrams, you will better understand how the table works. Once you are familiar with the methods explained in the diagrams, the table will eliminate the need physically to draw the cones.

Using a Protractor to find Spacing

For this explanation, we will:

- Draw a sectional view of the cone of light produced by a directional lamp with a 55° beam angle mounted in a recessed can 5 feet above the workplane.

- Determine the optimum spacing between lamps for general lighting.

- Find the location of the first lamp off the wall.

- Show how to allow for the depth of wall cabinetry.

The beam angle of 55° is chosen arbitrarily; any beam angle can be used in the technique. However, you will see that a beam angle of 55° works best with a ceiling height of 8 feet. The only difference between lamps of various beam angles will be the spacing between lamps... which is exactly the point of this discussion. The diagrams are printed in 1/2 inch scale for reference.

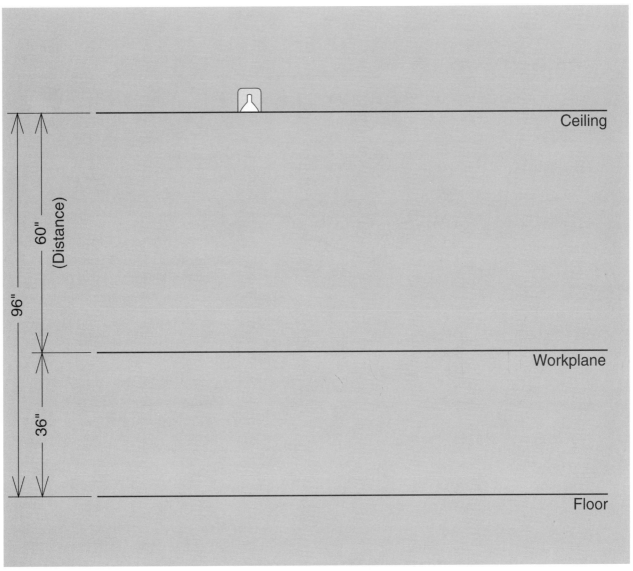

Figure 3.4   ***Draw the floor, workplane, and ceiling lines***

Step 1

Draw the floor line, the workplane (at 36 inches), and the ceiling line (at 96 inches.) Place a dot on the ceiling line somewhere near the center of the page (left to right) to indicate the first lamp. This dot is indicated by the recessed can in the diagrams. Don't worry that the wall has not been established yet; it comes later.

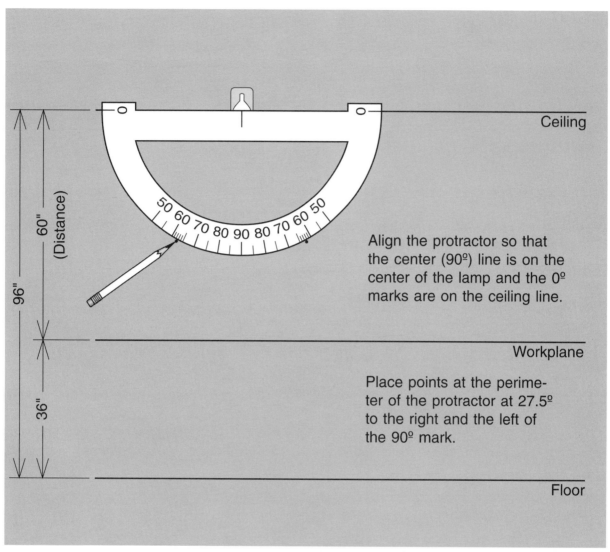

Ceiling

50 60 70 80 90 80 70 60 50

Align the protractor so that the center (90º) line is on the center of the lamp and the 0º marks are on the ceiling line.

96"

60" (Distance)

Workplane

Place points at the perimeter of the protractor at 27.5º to the right and the left of the 90º mark.

36"

Floor

Figure 3.5   Use a protractor to mark the beam angle

Step 2

Place a protractor on the page so that the vertical axis line (above the 90° mark) is lined up with the dot placed on the ceiling. At the same time, align the 0 degree marks (on the left and right of the protractor) so that they are on the ceiling line. Your protractor may differ from the one depicted. It won't matter as long as it is aligned in this manner.

For down lighting, the cone will need to be drawn perpendicular to the workplane.

Half the cone must be drawn to the right of center (nadir) and half to the left. To do this, divide the beam angle (55°) in half (27.5°). Find the 90° marking on the protractor, bottom center, and count off 27.5° to the right and mark a dot. The size of the protractor doesn't matter as long as the mark is placed on the paper directly on the perimeter of the protractor at the 27.5° indication. Now repeat the process for the left side of the cone.

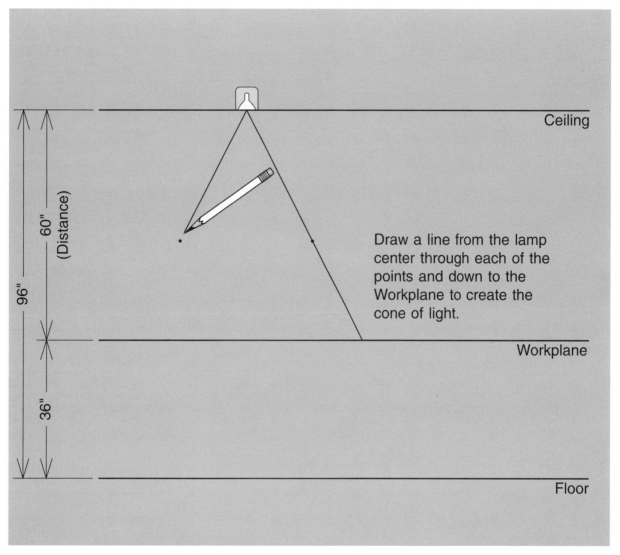

Draw a line from the lamp center through each of the points and down to the Workplane to create the cone of light.

Figure 3.6   **Draw the cone of light**

Step 3

Draw a line from the dot on the ceiling (lamp center) through each 27.5° dot so that it continues down to the workplane. This defines the sides of the cone. The cone of light for the first lamp is now complete, drawn perpendicular to workplane, at the 55° beam angle of the lamp.

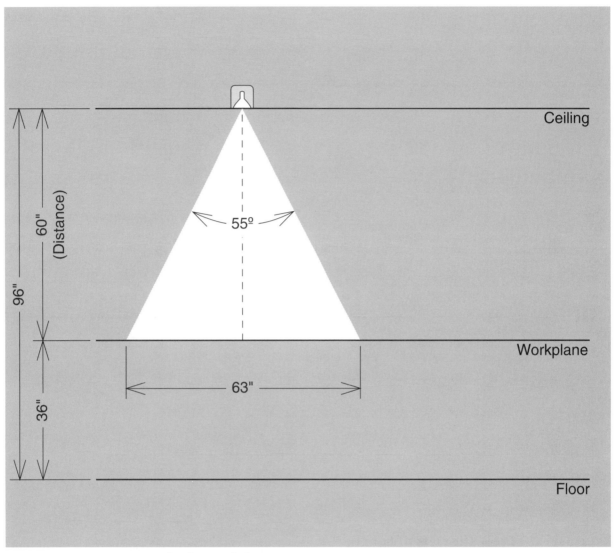

Figure 3.7   *Measure the base of the cone*

Step 4

To find the maximum spacing between lamps, measure the width of the cone as it sits on the workplane. If your cone is drawn correctly, the base should measure 63 inches.

If a second cone is drawn, so that it meets the first cone at the workplane, the spacing between the lamps will be 63 inches.

When the second 55° cone meets the first cone at the workplane, a third triangle is created in between. This third triangle is identical to the first two except that it is upside down with its base on the ceiling. This is why, due to the wonder of geometry, the second cone never really needs to be drawn. Once you have measured the base of the first cone, you have the maximum spacing.

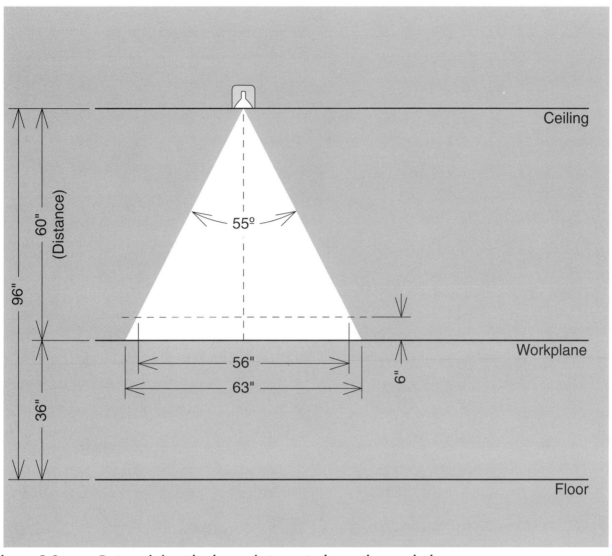

Figure 3.8   ***Determining the beam intersect above the workplane***

Step 5

Consider for a moment the fact that items do not rest within the countertop; rather, they sit upon it. To ensure that objects at the point where two cones meet will be illuminated evenly, space the cones so that they intersect 6 inches above the workplane.

To find the spacing which allows for the 6 inch intersect, measure 6 inches up from the workplane and draw a dashed line across the cone. Now measure the width of the cone at the dashed line. The measurement should be 56 inches.

TIP Cones of light should intersect above the work-plane for best coverage.

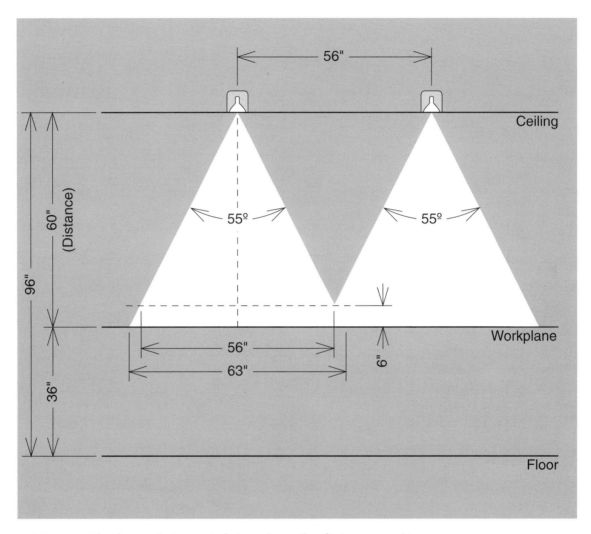

Figure 3.9 *The beam intersect determines the fixture spacing*

Step 6

If another 55° cone is drawn so that it intersects with the first cone 6 inches above the workplane, its center will be 56 inches away. Notice that the inverted triangle between the two cones is now identical to the original cone when measured from the dashed line up to the ceiling, the base of which is 56 inches.

If the lamps are placed throughout an area at 56 inches on center, the intersect will consistently be 6 inches above the workplane.

Of course this would be ideal, but there are things called joists, gas lines, and ducting which often prevent an ideal placement. Allow the intersect to be anywhere from 0 inches to 18 inches above the workplane (6 inches being ideal) to accommodate such obstacles. The more the cones overlap, however, the more noticeable the brightness at the intersection becomes.

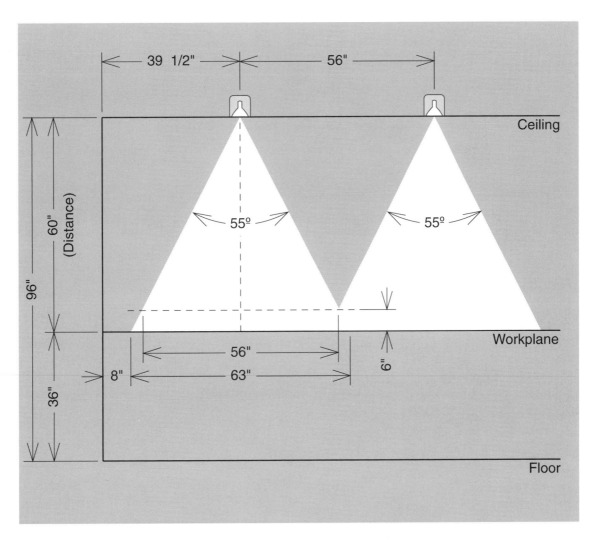

Figure 3.10   *Finding the spacing from the wall to the first fixture*

Step 7

The next problem is how far to place the first fixture from the wall while allowing for the depth of wall cabinets, if any.

At the workplane, find the bottom left point of the first cone we drew. Measure 8 inches to the left horizontally. This will become the wall if wall cabinets are present. The 8 inches is a constant derived from my own experience that always seems to work. Draw the vertical wall line. If there are no wall cabinets, the left edge of the cone becomes the wall.

The base of the original cone was 63 inches. Since we are concerned with the measurement from the center of the cone to the wall, divide the 63 inches in half, yielding 31.5 inches. By adding the constant (8 inches) to 31.5 inches, the spacing from the wall to the first fixture will be 39.5 inches. If no wall cabinets are present, the spacing to the first cone will be 31.5 inches.

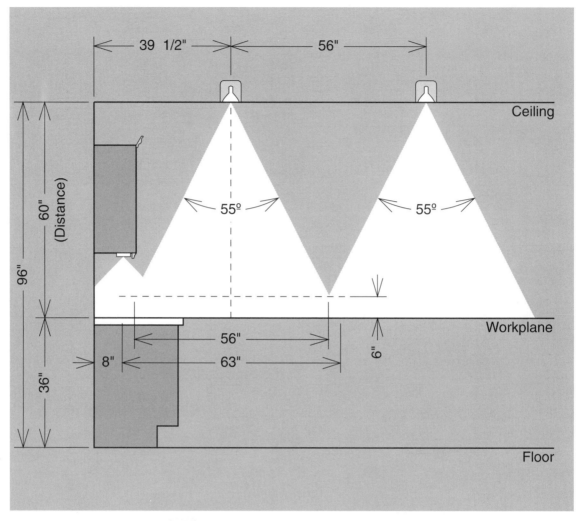

Figure 3.11   Allowing for wall cabinets and counter lighting

Step 8

To see how the cone of light relates to the wall cabinets, draw a section view of a typical base and wall cabinet against the wall which was located in Figure 3.10. Notice that, by holding the wall back 8 inches, the original cone of light does not intersect the face of the wall cabinet. If the 8 inch constant is not used, the cone will intersect the wall cabinet face and the result will be a scallop of light on the face of the cabinet. This is considered a "bad" thing. See Chapter 1 for a more detailed discussion of this issue.

Through the use of under-cabinet lighting, brighter task illumination of the countertop will be achieved. Determining the actual light level will be covered in Chapter 4.

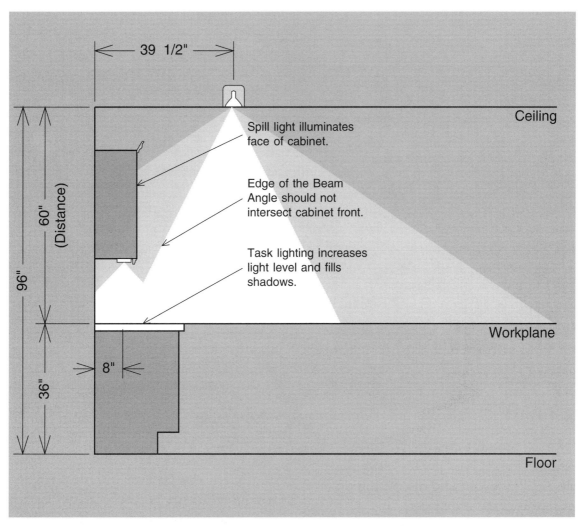

Figure 3.12 ___Preventing scallops while illuminating the wall cabinets___

Step 9

Recognize the relationship of the spill light to the face of the cabinetry. Spill light is adequate to illuminate the face of the cabinets without causing the harsh scallops. Specifying a white or light cabinet interior will allow the light that enters the cabinet to reflect inside, increasing the light level to the interior.

In working through the previous diagrams, you will have gained an understanding of the geometry used in constructing and spacing the cones of light generated by directional lamps based on their beam angle and the distance they are placed above the workplane.

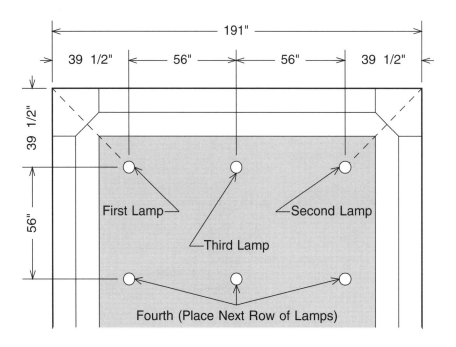

Figure 3.13   Ideal order of placement

Step 10

Let's see how the spacing we have worked out might look in plan view in a simple kitchen layout and discuss the order in which the lamps are placed.

We know that the first lamp off the wall will be 39.5 inches. Starting in the corner, the first lamp will be placed 39.5 inches from either wall, placing it on the bisection line of the corner. This will look quite nice since both the lamp and the diagonal wall cabinet will be viewed together. This also sets up a relationship; lamp, ceiling, room corner, and diagonal wall cabinet. Anywhere this relationship occurs again in the room should be treated in like fashion. An ideal kitchen would allow the target 56 inches between any ensuing lamp pairs and end with a 39.5 inch dimension.

Placing three lamps across a "U" shape kitchen would require a room 191 inches wide. Now that this trio of fixtures is located, you can simply repeat them throughout the room in like manner.

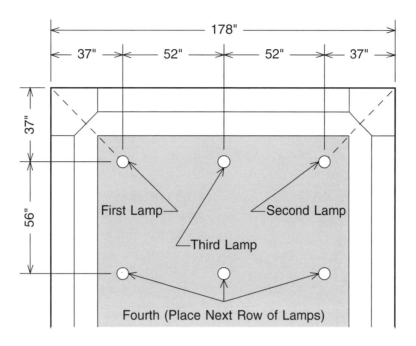

Figure 3.14   Placement with a mix of reality

Step 11

Well... wasn't that convenient. Now let's look at a more realistic example.

In this case, the room is 178 inches. When 39.5 inches is subtracted for both corners, the result is 99 inches which is not divisible evenly by 56 inches . There are two choices available at this point: change the beam angle of the lamp or adjust the spacing to fit the 55° beam angle we have been working with. It is not a perfect world and often we must compromise to fit the situation.

This will require a bit of a hunt-and-peck approach, but it is part of lighting design. A dimension of 37 inches by 37 inches has been selected for the lamps at the corners. In

looking at Figure 3.11, there is some leeway between the edge of the cone and the face of the cabinetry. The new 37 inch dimension will still prevent scalloping.

Subtracting the 37 inch dimension, once for each corner, from the 178 inch room width leaves 104 inches. Dividing 104 inches in half yields 52 inches which is not too far off our target 56 inches. What we have done is moved the intersect point up a couple of inches, but still within the recommended 0 inch to 18 inch tolerance. This is a good compromise of all factors involved. We now have a new relationship for the trio of lights at the end of the kitchen and it can be repeated throughout the room as was discussed in Step 10.

One thing to note is that the trio of light can be placed at the new 52 inch interval or the original 56 inches. While the ceiling grid is best done in squares for even light, often the realistic solution will be rectangles considering the length and width of the room independently. The example shows a 52 inch by 56 inch grid pattern.

Using the Spacing Table

The Spacing Table can replace the process of using a protractor to lay out the cones of light to determine the spacing. It also makes much simpler the job of laying out task lighting for specific areas, over an island, for example. It is appropriate to talk about the use of the Spacing Table only after understanding the geometry involved in spacing the cones of light.

To use the Spacing Table, Figure 3.15, it is necessary to know the beam angle of the intended lamp and the distance it is to be placed above the workplane. The top row of the Table lists the beam angle (in degrees) with the distances (in feet) down the left side. Remember that these are distance measurements, **not** ceiling heights. Where the beam angle and the distance intersect is the maximum spacing, provided in inches for practicality.

Taking the 55° angle in the previous section as an example, the maximum spacing and spacing for the beam intersect above the workplane, locating the wall, and the first fixture off the wall can be found. The table can also be used to allow for wall cabinet depth.

Find the Spacing between Lamps

The example from the previous section used a 55° beam angle in a kitchen with an 8 foot ceiling. Follow the top row across the page to 55°. Now travel down this column to the row labeled 5 feet (the distance from the counter to the recessed can). The spacing indicated at this juncture is 63 inches. The 63 inches indicates the width of the cone as it rests on the workplane, which is the same as the maximum spacing. Using this spacing increment will cause the cones to meet at the workplane rather than the recommended 6 inches above the workplane.

Allowing for the Intersect

To allow for a 6 inch intersect above the workplane, instead of following the 55° column down to the 5 foot distance, follow it down to 4.5 feet. Think about it: if the cones intersect 6 inches above the workplane, the intersect is 4.5 feet from the lamp. At the 4.5 foot distance, the spacing is indicated as 56 inches. If the lamps are spaced at 56 inches, they will intersect 6 inches above the workplane.

Finding the Wall

The wall location can be found by taking the width of the cone, as it rests on the workplane (63 inches in this example), dividing it in half (31.5 inches) and adding the constant of 8 inches to allow for standard wall cabinet depth (refer to Figure 3.10). Half the cone (31.5 inches) plus the constant (8 inches) equals 39.5 inches, which is the spacing from the wall to the first fixture. Remember, if there are no wall cabinets, the spacing to the first fixture would be simply half the cone or 31.5 inches.

Spacing Table

Use this table to determine spacing when the intersect distance and beam angle are known **or** to find the beam angle when the desired spacing and intersect distance are known.

Beam Angle

Distance to intersect from lamp	1°	5°	10°	15°	20°	25°	30°	35°	40°	45°	50°	55°	60°	65°	70°	75°	80°	85°	90°	95°	100°
0.5'	.1"	.5"	1"	2"	2"	3"	3"	4"	4"	5"	6"	6"	7"	8"	8"	9"	10"	11"	12"	13"	14"
1'	.2"	1"	2"	3"	4"	5"	6"	8"	9"	10"	11"	12"	14"	15"	17"	18"	20"	22"	24"	26"	29"
1.5'	.4"	2"	3"	5"	6"	8"	10"	11"	13"	15"	17"	19"	21"	23"	25"	28"	30"	33"	36"	39"	43"
1.75'	.4"	2"	4"	6"	7"	9"	11"	13"	15"	17"	20"	22"	24"	27"	29"	32"	35"	39"	42"	46"	50"
2'	.4"	2"	4"	6"	9"	11"	13"	15"	18"	20"	22"	25"	28"	31"	34"	37"	40"	44"	48"	52"	57"
2.25'	.5"	2"	5"	7"	9"	12"	15"	17"	20"	22"	25"	28"	31"	34"	38"	41"	45"	49"	54"	59"	64"
2.5'	.5"	3"	5"	8"	11"	13"	16"	19"	22"	25"	28"	31"	35"	38"	42"	46"	50"	55"	60"	66"	72"
3'	1"	3"	6"	9"	13"	16"	19"	23"	26"	30"	34"	37"	42"	46"	50"	55"	60"	66"	72"	79"	86"
3.5'	1"	4"	7"	11"	15"	19"	23"	27"	31"	35"	39"	44"	48"	54"	59"	64"	70"	77"	84"	92"	100"
4'	1"	4"	8"	13"	17"	21"	26"	30"	35"	40"	45"	50"	55"	61"	67"	74"	81"	88"	96"	105"	114"
4.5'	1"	5"	9"	14"	19"	24"	29"	34"	39"	45"	50"	56"	62"	69"	76"	83"	91"	99"	108"	118"	129"
5'	1"	5"	10"	16"	21"	27"	32"	38"	44"	50"	56"	63"	69"	76"	84"	92"	101"	110"	120"	131"	143"
5.5'	1"	6"	12"	17"	23"	29"	35"	42"	48"	55"	62"	69"	76"	84"	92"	101"	111"	121"	132"	144"	157"
6'	1"	6"	13"	19"	25"	32"	39"	45"	52"	60"	67"	75"	83"	92"	101"	111"	121"	132"	144"	157"	172"
6.5'	1"	7"	14"	21"	27"	35"	42"	49"	57"	65"	73"	81"	90"	99"	109"	120"	131"	143"	156"	170"	186"
7'	1"	7"	15"	22"	30"	37"	45"	53"	61"	70"	78"	87"	97"	107"	118"	129"	141"	154"	168"	183"	200"
7.5'	2"	8"	16"	24"	32"	40"	48"	57"	66"	75"	84"	94"	104"	115"	126"	138"	151"	165"	180"	196"	215"
8'	2"	8"	17"	25"	34"	43"	51"	60"	70"	80"	90"	100"	111"	122"	134"	147"	161"	176"	192"	210"	229"
8.5'	2"	9"	18"	27"	36"	45"	55"	64"	74"	84"	95"	106"	118"	130"	143"	156"	171"	187"	204"	223"	243"
9'	2"	9"	19"	28"	38"	48"	58"	68"	79"	90"	101"	112"	125"	138"	151"	166"	181"	198"	216"	236"	257"
9.5'	2"	10"	20"	30"	40"	51"	61"	72"	83"	94"	106"	119"	132"	145"	160"	175"	191"	209"	228"	249"	272"
10'	2"	10"	21"	32"	42"	53"	64"	76"	87"	99"	112"	125"	139"	153"	168"	184"	201"	220"	240"	262"	286"

Δ ———————— Spacing Between Luminaires ———————— Δ

Figure 3.15

All the dimensions derived from the protractor exercise, then, can be found in a fraction of the time through using the table.

Find the Beam Angle for the Desired Spacing

You can also use the table if you want to find the beam angle that will produce a spacing that you dictate! Say the spacing you have determined for the location of ceiling trusses is 48 inches on center, and you would like the cones to intersect 6 inches above the workplane. Since the intersect is 4.5 feet from the lamp, travel across the 4.5 foot row until you find 48 inches. The closest dimension to 48 inches is 50 inches. Travel up the 50 inch column to find the beam angle which is 50°. A lamp with a 50° beam angle will produce a cone that, when spaced at 50 inches, will intersect at 6 inches above the workplane.

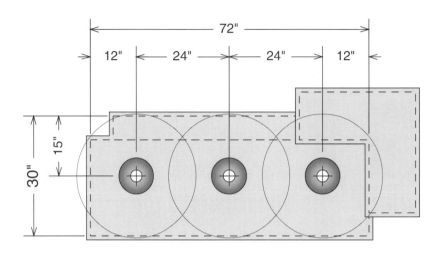

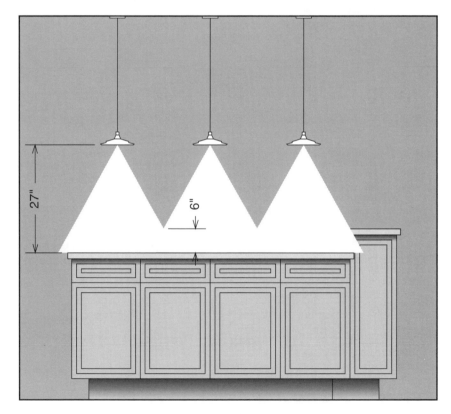

Figure 3.16   **Task lighting at an island**

Directional Lamps and Task Lighting

The Spacing Table can also be used to find the beam angle necessary to provide a predetermined spacing necessary due to the fixed dimensions of an island, the width of the counter area between wall cabinets at a window, or across a bathroom pullman counter. The next section will deal with spacing issues for such task oriented situations using the Spacing Table to determine the beam angle. Understand that it is possible to do the following examples with a protractor, but so much faster with the Spacing Table.

Task lighting differs little from the way general lighting is handled. It is still a matter of seeing to it that the beam angle emanating from a lamp placed at a given distance above the workplane evenly covers the intended area. Rather than the walls being the bounds within which the lamps are placed, the workplane itself becomes the boundary of the brighter task lighting field. Lets' look at an island to see how it works.

Figure 3.16 shows an island with a working surface 30 inches wide by 72 inches long. Pendants are a nice choice for this application because the lamps can be placed at a distance above the workplane so that they provide the proper footcandle level (more on that in Chapter 4) and contrast to the recessed general lighting. This helps to define an island as a focal point.

We will use an MR16 lamp in the pendant due to the diversity of beam angles and candlepower available. A pendant should be placed between 24 inches to 27 inches above an island to keep it below eye level. MR16 lamps are bright and uncomfortable to look at, to say the least. Thinking in terms of half cones, and *arbitrarily*

selecting three pendants, let's see how the spacing works out. By dividing the number of half cones (6) into the length of the island (72 inches), the width of each half cone is determined to be 12 inches. This will provide a spacing of 24 inches between lamps. However, 24 inches is not wide enough to cover the depth of the counter. So, we need to find a beam angle that, when placed 27 inches above the counter, will create a circle of light on the counter surface that is about 30 inches in diameter.

If the lamp is to be placed 27 inches above the counter, then 27 inches becomes the distance. Using the Spacing Table, figure 3.15, find the distance row marked 2.25 feet (27 inches), and travel across it to find the column with the closest beam diameter to the target 30 inches island width. You will find a column showing 31 inches. Travel up this column to find that the beam angle will be 60°. Don't forget, by spacing the lamps 24 inches apart, we have created an intersect height above the island surface. To determine whether it is in the desired range, find 31 inches again on the Spacing Table (the point where 60° and 2.25 feet meet) and travel up the column until you find 24 inches. You are now in the 1.75 foot (21 inches) distance row, or 6 inches up: perfect.

We will look at this island example again in Chapter 4. There we will determine what candlepower the lamp must be to provide an adequate amount of light for kitchen related task activities.

Under-Cabinet Task Lighting

There are several considerations when designing under-cabinet lighting for task counters. The lighting must be distributed evenly along the counter surface, the backsplash should also be lit evenly, and the wiring to the fixtures should be reasonably hidden.

There is a great variety of fixture and lamp types intended for under-cabinet lighting and we should take a moment and consider them and the ramifications of their placement. Remembering that spacing is always about triangles and circles; it only makes sense that the counter lighting be in the center of the counter. If the counter is 24 inches deep, then the lamps should be placed about 12 inches out from the wall. In this fashion, the entire depth of the counter will be illuminated evenly. However, with countertops come backsplashes. The back-splash is frequently a focal point and needs to be considered in fixture selection and placement as well.

While the under-cabinet lighting provides a more intense footcandle level to the counter, it also is the primary light source for the backsplash and affects how it appears. Always place the lamps behind the light rail and not directly against the backsplash. In doing so, the light has more space to diffuse before it hits the backsplash. This reduces the "pools" of light separated by dark areas which really detract from the visual continuity of the entire room. The more tightly spaced the lamps, the more even the lighting on the backsplash. I rec-ommend 2 inch spacing for two reasons. It is easy to fit the length of a run of cabinets (much easier than fixtures that only come in 12 inches, 18 inches, 24 inches, etc.) and it produces a very even field of light, not only on the counter, but on the backsplash as well. Look to the *Lamps and Fixtures* Chap-ter for more information on under-cabinet fixture types

Hiding wires is also a major concern. No matter where you sit in a room, some portion of the bottom of the wall cabinets

will be visible. Wiring is ugly and electricians love BIG staples. While this topic doesn't necessarily fit into a chapter devoted to spacing, it is part of the selection process which does affect spacing. Fixtures that come in long strips which can be trimmed to length every few inches are the best for running concealed wire. Only at the end of a wall cabinet run does the wire have to connect. Wall cabinets often terminate at appliance garages and tall cabinets such as pantries, oven cases, built-in refrigerators, etc. Feeding the under-cabinet fixture through these cabinets will hide the wires.

Omni-Directional Lamps

Omni-directional lamps, like fluorescent and compact fluorescent, are typically used for general lighting. Omni-directional lamps do not produce a beam angle, and consequently there is no way to use the Spacing Table to help you locate them. However, in Chapter 4, there is a calculation for determining the ideal spacing for such lamps and the fixtures that hold them. Once the spacing is calculated, think of it as the beam diameter at the workplane and proceed as you did for direc-tional lamps. It isn't scientifically proven, but will act as a reliable guide.

Some Final Thoughts

You now have a working knowledge of how to space lamps based on the distance they are placed above the workplane and the beam angle, so that they distribute the light evenly with adequate coverage. Chapter 4 will discuss how to determine the footcandle level needed for a room or activity and how to find a lamp powerful enough to provide it.

QUIZ

1. Why is spacing important?
   a.) To illuminate the area evenly.
   b.) To ensure proper coverage of a surface or object.
   c.) To determine the number of fixtures.
   d.) All of the above.

2. Rules of spacing apply to general and task lighting, as well as, recessed and pendant fixtures?
   T   F

3. It is appropriate to consider spacing in terms of?
   a.) 1/2 cones.
   b.) 1/4 cones.
   c.) Ice cream cones.
   d.) Cones of silence.

4. How many cones occur between pairs of lamps?
   a.) Three 1/4 cones.
   b.) One 3/5 cone.
   c.) Mass quantities.
   d.) Two 1/2 cones.

5. If cones of light do not meet at the workplane, ...?
   a.) there will be a rift in the space/time continuum.
   b.) there will be a gap of light resulting in a dark area.
   c.) there will never be little cones.
   d.) shadowing will occur.

6. For general lighting, a good spacing between fixtures is?
   a.) 30" - 60".
   b.) The ceiling surface divided equally.
   c.) 48" - 72".
   d.) Enough to maintain security clearance.

7. What is the acceptable cone intersect range above the workplane?
   _____"   to   _____"

8. What is the optimum cone intersect height.
   _____"

9. With a protractor, at a distance of 5', draw the cones of light for lamps with beam angles of 10 degrees, 29 degrees, and 53 degrees. What will be the maximum spacing for each beam angle?
   10 degrees   _____"
   29 degrees   _____"
   53 degrees   _____"

10. For the lamps in question 9, what will be the spacing with a 6" intersect above the workplane?
    10 degrees   _____"
    29 degrees   _____"
    53 degrees   _____"

11. For the lamps in question 9, what will be the spacing from the wall to the first lamp when wall cabinets are present?

   10 degrees   ____ "

   29 degrees   ____ "

   53 degrees   ____ "

Use the Spacing Table, Figure 3.15, to find the following:

12. The distance to the workplane is 5' and recessed fixtures are to be used. The desired spacing is 56" with a 6" cone intersect above the workplane. What is the beam angle?

   ____ °

13. The distance to the workplane is 6' and recessed fixtures are to be used. The desired spacing is 56" with a 6" cone intersect above the workplane. What is the beam angle?

   ____ °

14. The distance to the workplane is 7' and recessed fixtures are to be used. The desired spacing is 56" with a 6" cone intersect above the workplane. What is the beam angle?

   ____ °

15. What beam angle produces a 32" diameter circle on the workplane at a 5' distance?

   ____ °

16. What beam angle produces a 24" diameter circle on the workplane at a 5' distance?

   ____ °

17. What will be the spacing between lamps in question 15 with a 6" intersect?

   ____ "

18. What will be the spacing between lamps in question 16 with a 6" intersect?

   ____ "

19. What is the spacing from the wall to the first lamp (when wall cabinets are present) using a lamp with a 40° beam angle at a 6' distance?

   ____ "

20. When using omni-directional lamps where there is no beam angle, how is the spacing determined?

   _____

   _____

   _____

   _____

   _____

   _____

   _____

   _____

   _____

   _____

   _____

   _____

   _____

   _____

See *Solutions* in the back of the book for answers and explanations.

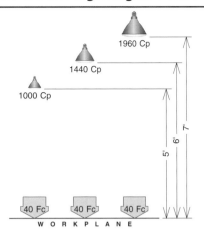

CHAPTER 4

LIGHTING MEASUREMENTS

In Chapter 1 we discussed various lighting concepts, Chapter 2 dealt with color, and Chapter 3 introduced the beam angle with spacing techniques. You may be wondering when is it that we will actually start to design with lamps and fixtures. Be comforted... that time is upon us!

It is through this Chapter that you will become familiar, and hopefully comfortable with, the simple calculations necessary to provide before the start of construction, a lighting plan with the confidence that it will work well. So retire those jeans with the dirty knees soiled from so much praying that your project will have enough light. Although the calculations are simple, the information is presented in what might be perceived as a laborious step-by-step process. It is better to over explain than to assume the experience of the reader.

As we have learned, the primary goal in lighting design is to provide an adequate amount of light to the space we are illuminating. More accurately, it is to match the appropriate lamp and fixture together with a fixture trim to provide the correct Footcandle level for the activity/activities that will occur in the room. Once this is done, a lamp with enough power to maintain the Footcandle level throughout the space or across the task area must be found. You will use **either** the Inverse Square Law **or** the Lumen Method to do this.

The topics in this Chapter are:

- **Footcandle Levels**

- **Inverse Square Law**

- **Lumen Method**

In the section dealing with the Inverse Square Law and the Lumen Method, recommendations will be made regarding when each is to be used.

Room	Activity	Base Footcandle Level
Art		50
	* Or five times greater than the surrounding illumination.	*
Bath		
	General, Make-up, Shaving	30
	Full Length Mirror	30
Desk		
	Casual	30
	Study	75
Dining		15
Family Room		
	General	7.5
	Table Games	30
Hall/Passage		7.5
Handicrafts		
	Ordinary Tasks	30
	Difficult Tasks/Easel Work	75
	Critical Tasks	150
Kitchen		
	General	30
	Task	75
Laundry		30
Living Room		7.5
Music		
	Simple Scores	30
	Advanced Scores	75
	Sub-standard Size Scores	150
Reading		
	Books, Magazines, Newspapers	30
	Handwriting, Prolonged	75
Sewing		
	Occasional, High Contrast	30
	Light to Medium Fabrics	75
	Dark Fabrics, Low Contrast	150

Table 4.1   Recommended base footcandle levels

Footcandle Level

As discussed in Chapter 1, the footcandle level is measured on the surface to be illuminated. This surface can be a kitchen counter, bathroom vanity, dining table, an implied horizontal plane in a living or family room, or art on a wall.

The IES (Illuminating Engineering Society) has recommended optimum footcandle levels for every room of the home which are listed in Table 4.1. Note that the levels in the Table are **base** levels and will need some further adjustment. More on that in a bit.

Adjusting the Footcandle Level

Table 4.2 gives the IES recommended adjustments for three categories: occupant age, average room reflectance (average ceiling, wall, and floor), and background reflectance (counter color). Adjustments must be made cumulatively; in other words, adjust the base footcandle level for occupant age, then adjust the new level for average room reflectance, then adjust this newest level for background reflectance. The following example will make the process clear.

Occupant Age and Reflectance		*Adjustment Factor*		
		.66	**1**	**1.33**
1	*Occupant Age*	Under 40	40-55	Over 55
2	*Average Room Reflectance* (Average Ceiling, Walls, Floor)	Over 70% *Light*	30-70% *Medium*	Under 30% *Dark*
3	*Task Background Reflectance* (Counter Color)	Over 70% *Light*	30-70% *Medium*	Under 30% *Dark*

Table 4.2   Adjustment factors for base footcandle levels

To find the recommended base footcandle level, locate in Table 4.1 the room to be illuminated, then determine the closest activity for the intended project. For example, if the room is to be a music study, locate "Music" in the table and then decide whether the usual sheet music will be "Simple Scores" (30 Fc), "Advanced Scores" (75 Fc), or "Sub-Standard Sized Scores" (150 Fc). If the selection is "Advanced Scores," then the base footcandle level is 75.

Example:

We will use a kitchen with an average room reflectance of 75% and a dark gray countertop which has a reflectance of 10% - 15%. We want to determine the appropriate footcandle level for general, task, and art lighting in the room.

In the Footcandle Table 4.1, we see the following recommended footcandle levels for lighting in the kitchen:

General	*Task*
Base = 30 Fc	Base = 75 Fc

These are the base footcandle levels and both must be adjusted for occupant age, average room reflectance, and background reflectance. The following explanations discuss the adjustment process.

Adjusting for Occupant Age

Always use an occupant age of "over 55" to be consistent with universal design philosophy. The idea is that all clients, if not 55 already, will reach 55 at some point or will have friends or relatives who are. They may sell their home to a couple in the 55-and-older age bracket.

 **TIP** Use "over 55" when adjusting the Fc level for universal design.

At age 55, the eyes will require more light to do any task. By using "over 55," an occupant of any age will be accommodated suitably by the lighting scheme. It is always possible to use a less powerful lamp in a fixture, but sometimes a more powerful lamp cannot be installed in a fixture originally specified for a less powerful lamp.

Using the Footcandle Adjustment Table 4.2, adjust the general and task Fc levels for occupant age. Find "over 55" in row 1 of the table, then follow the column up to its corresponding adjustment factor; in this case, 1.33. Multiply the base Fc level for general and then for task by 1.33.

General	*Task*
30 x 1.33 = 40 Fc	75 x 1.33 = 100 Fc

Unfortunately, the colors or materials often are not known when the lighting plan is drawn. When the colors and their reflectances are not known, consider them to be "medium (30-70%.)"

 **TIP** When the reflectances of a room are not known, use "medium (30-70%)"

Since rows 2 and 3 of Table 4.2, which deal with the reflectance levels for the room, use an adjustment factor of 1 for the medium range, there is no point in continuing. The levels will remain the same. So, if we did not know the colors of the materials in our example kitchen, the general lighting Fc level would remain 40 and task, 100. It is for this reason that I use 40 and 100 Fc as a "rule-of-the-road" in the kitchen for general and task lighting respectively.

 **TIP** If reflectances are not known, use:

	General	Task
Kitchen	40 Fc	100 Fc
Bath	40 Fc	

Adjusting for Overall Reflectance

Since light reflects off the surfaces of objects back into the room, the reflected light **adds** to the overall light level and must be accounted for. A black or "dark" colored room reflects 4% while a white or "light" room reflects 80%. This makes a tremendous difference on the number of lamps required to achieve a given lighting level.

Our example kitchen has an average room reflectance of 75%. In row 2 of Table 4.2, notice that 75% falls within the range "over 70%," which is in the column with an adjustment factor of .66. Multiply the previously adjusted general and task Fc levels from row 1 by .66.

General **Task**
40 x .66 = 26 Fc   100 x .66 = 66 Fc

Adjusting for Background Reflectance

The counter surface or "background reflectance" acts as a backdrop to the work activity in the room and its contrast affects one's ability to see comfortably in either general or task activities. Think of the black letters on this white page as opposed to black letters on a gray page. Due to the greater contrast, the white page will require less light to read at the same comfort level than the gray page.

Continuing with the example kitchen, the countertop is dark gray. Looking back, to the reflectance Table 2.6 in Chapter 2, dark gray has a reflectance of 10%-15%. Looking now in row 3 of Table 4.2, find that 10%-15% falls "under 30%" which is in the column with an adjustment factor of 1.33. Multiply the previously adjusted general and task Fc levels from Row 2 by 1.33 to obtain the adjusted Fc level for Row 3.

General **Task**
26 x 1.33 = 35 Fc   66 x 1.33 = 88 Fc

Adjusted Footcandle Level

The footcandle level for general and task lighting have now been cumulatively adjusted for occupant age, average room reflectance, and background reflectance. The adjusted Fc levels for the example kitchen are:

General **Task**
Adjusted = 35 Fc   Adjusted = 88 Fc

The adjusted Fc levels for the example kitchen did not vary greatly from the base levels originally found in Table 4.1. However, if the conditions in the room were such that all three adjustment factors were .66 or 1.33, the results would have been drastically different. General lighting would have ranged from a low of 9 Fc to a high of 70 Fc while task would have run from a low of 22 Fc to a high of 176 Fc respectively!

Always take the time to adjust the base footcandle levels for best results.

Art Lighting Levels

When lighting art, it should have the appearance of being highlighted or accented. In order to achieve this, the footcandle level must be 5 times greater than the surrounding light level.

 **TIP** Art lighting should be 5 times brighter than the surrounding light.

If the art is to be placed in the kitchen, the footcandle level on the art needs to be 5 times the adjusted general footcandle level. For our example kitchen, 5 times the adjusted general Fc level (35) yields an art Fc requirement of 175.

General	*Art*
Adjusted 35 Fc	5 x 35 = 175 Fc

Never use less than 50 footcandles for art lighting. For example, a living room needs only 7.5 footcandles for general lighting. Even though 5 times 7.5 equals 38, the minimum art footcandle level should be increased to 50.

In either case, the art footcandle level for the kitchen (175 Fc), or the living room (50 Fc), will appear to have the same illumination because it is the contrast ratio (5:1) between the art and general lighting that our eyes perceive as highlight.

Now What?

Now that the footcandle level has been established, it is possible to start the process of looking for a lamp that will produce it. We will first look at the Inverse Square Law which can only be used for directional lamps; those having a candlepower rating. It can be used for general or task lighting scenarios. Then we will delve into the Lumen Method which can be used anytime the manufacturer supplies an efficiency specification known as a CU (Coefficient of Utilization) rating. Don't panic... CU will be explained later. The Lumen Method is used for general illumination.

In Chapter 3, *Spacing Principles*, we determined how far apart the lamps or fixtures should be spaced to maintain an even field of light across a specified area, such as an island, or the entire room. It is now our job to make sure that the footcandle level produced under **each** of the lamps is appropriate. Ultimately, you will select a lamp that produces the footcandle level necessary **and** that fits your spacing requirements.

Inverse Square Law

Now that you are able to set a footcandle level, the next step is to find a lamp powerful enough to provide it. The important thing to remember is that the greater the distance the lamp is from the object or workplane, the more powerful it will need to be.

 **TIP** The greater the distance a lamp is from the workplane, the more powerful it needs to be.

The Inverse Square Law is a formula which allows the designer to establish the appropriate lamp candlepower for any distance the lamp is placed above the workplane (or object to be illuminated) in order to achieve the desired footcandle level. It can be used with directional lamps having a candlepower rating (i.e., floods, spots, PAR, MR16, etc.).

The three variables the Inverse Square Law takes into consideration are:

- **Candlepower**   **(Cp)**

- **Footcandle**   **(Fc)**

- **Distance**   **(D)**

The formula can solve for any one of the variables if the other two are known. So there are actually three formulas; one solving for each unknown variable:

Candlepower = D^2 x Fc   *or*

Footcandles =   Cp ÷ D^2 *or*

Distance   = $\sqrt{Cp ÷ Fc}$

Solving for Candlepower

Suppose we have a kitchen that will require 40 Fc for general illumination and that will use recessed cans in an 8 foot ceiling. The formula solving for candlepower will give the candlepower required of a lamp to produce 40 Fc on a workplane 5 feet below the lamp. Remember the workplane is the counter at 3 feet which leaves 5 feet from the counter surface to the ceiling. In this case we know the Fc level (40) and the distance (5 feet). The remaining unknown is candlepower. Simply plug the Fc level and distance into the formula to find Cp:

8 foot ceiling:

Candlepower	=	D^2 x Fc
	=	5^2 x 40
	=	25 x 40
	=	1000 Cp

Now let's raise the ceiling to 9 feet. The distance will increase to 6 feet, but the footcandle level will remain the same since it is still a kitchen regardless of the ceiling/lamp height. Reworking the formula for the new distance will look like this:

9 foot ceiling:

Candlepower	=	D^2 x Fc
	=	6^2 x 40
	=	36 x 40
	=	1440 Cp

By raising the ceiling to 10 feet, the distance will increase to 7 feet, the Fc level remains at 40. Reworking the formula for the new distance will now appear:

10 foot ceiling:

Candlepower	=	D^2 x Fc
	=	7^2 x 40
	=	49 x 40
	=	1960 Cp

Interestingly, you will never again need to work these distances for a kitchen requiring 40 Fc. They never change! Knowing the formula, however, enables you to find the Cp level for any Fc level at any distance.

Look at figure 4.3 and think vaulted ceilings. Many designers make the mistake of using the same lamp candlepower across a vaulted ceiling which causes one side of the room to be severely underlit. By raising the lamp only 2 feet, the Cp requirement has almost doubled!

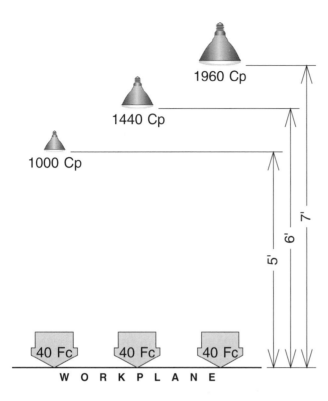

Figure 4.3 *Increasing distances need increasing Cp to maintain the same Fc*

Solving for Footcandles

Let's look at what happens when the same lamp (1000 Cp) is used at the three ceiling heights (8 feet, 9 feet, 10 feet).

We now know the Cp (1000) and the three distances (5 feet, 6 feet, 7 feet). Plug the knowns into the formula that solves for Footcandles.

8 foot ceiling:

$$
\begin{aligned}
\text{Footcandle} &= Cp \div D^2 \\
&= 1000 \div 5^2 \\
&= 1000 \div 25 \\
&= 40 \text{ Fc}
\end{aligned}
$$

9 foot ceiling:

$$
\begin{aligned}
\text{Footcandle} &= Cp \div D^2 \\
&= 1000 \div 6^2 \\
&= 1000 \div 36 \\
&= 28 \text{ Fc}
\end{aligned}
$$

10 foot ceiling:

$$
\begin{aligned}
\text{Footcandle} &= Cp \div D^2 \\
&= 1000 \div 7^2 \\
&= 1000 \div 49 \\
&= 20 \text{ Fc}
\end{aligned}
$$

Figure 4.4 graphically represents the results of the above calculations.

Rather than acquiring a lamp with a different Cp for each height, a possible solution might be to average the ceiling height and select a lamp for the mean height. For example, in Figure 4.4, choosing a lamp that will produce the desired Fc level for the 6 foot distance will provide better overall illumination than the depicted results.

In an imaginary world where there were lamps of any conceivable candlepower, the best results would be had if the candlepower increased as the distance increased yielding a constant footcandle level as shown in figure 4.3.

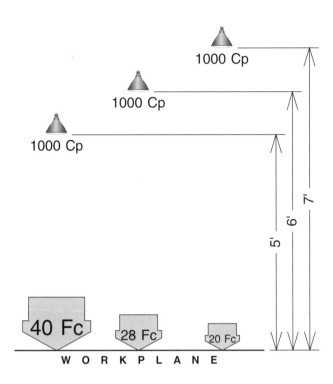

Figure 4.4 ***Increasing distances at the same Cp yield decreasing Fc***

1960 Cp:

Footcandle	=	Cp ÷ D^2
	=	1960 ÷ 5^2
	=	1960 ÷ 25
	=	78 Fc

Figure 4.5 gives a visual representation of the calculations above.

The previous exercises make it clear that candlepower, footcandle, and distance have a specific relationship and, by using the Inverse Square Law, it is demonstrated that when any one of them is changed, the other two are affected.

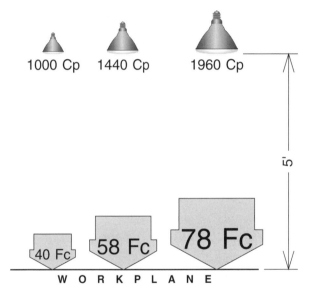

Figure 4.5 ***Increasing Cp at the same distance will yield increasing Fc***

Let's use the lamps from figure 4.3 and apply the formula that solves for footcandles once more to see the information in another way. This time the distance will remain the same (5 feet) and the Cp will change.

1000 Cp:

Footcandle	=	Cp ÷ D^2
	=	1000 ÷ 5^2
	=	1000 ÷ 25
	=	40 Fc

1440 Cp:

Footcandle	=	Cp ÷ D^2
	=	1440 ÷ 5^2
	=	1440 ÷ 25
	=	58 Fc

Solving for Distance

As yet we have not looked at the third formula, the one that solves for distance. It comes into play when you want to know exactly how high above a surface to place a lamp to get an exact Fc level. For example, if we had a 20 foot ceiling height, and could hang a pendant at any height above the workplane, and we wanted to produce 100 footcandles on an island for task lighting, and the lamp we wanted to use produced 1500 Cp, what would be the correct distance?

First we have to determine what we know and what we need to know. We know the Fc level (100) and we know the lamp candlepower (1500). What is not known is the distance. Use the formula which solves for distance and insert the known information:

$$
\begin{aligned}
\text{Distance} \quad &= \sqrt{Cp \div Fc} \\
&= \sqrt{1500 \div 100} \\
&= \sqrt{15} \\
&= \quad 3.87' \ \textit{or} \ 46 \, 1/2"
\end{aligned}
$$

The formula tells us that the pendant, when hung so the lamp is 46 1/2 inches above the island top, will provide 100 Fc to the surface.

Finding a Suitable Lamp Using the Inverse Square Law

Finding a lamp is simple once the candlepower is known. All that is necessary is to look through either a manufacturer's lamp specification or, the ever so wonderful, *Appendix A* in this book.

Appendix A provides the necessary lamp information used in the calculations described in this chapter, as well as, Spacing and Reflectance data. Be sure to read the "Appendix Conventions."

The most convenient feature of the Appendix, however, is a method for quickly finding those lamps that are the most efficient while offering the best color qualities. If the lamp entry is preceded by a Ⓔ or a △, it either meets or is exempted from the energy guidelines set forth by EPACT (Energy Policy Act of 1992). If the lamp is also preceded by a ☺, it meets all the recommendations from Chapter 2 regarding CRI and Color Temperature. Using only those lamps exhibiting two symbols Ⓔ ☺ or △ ☺ will eliminate 75% of the lamps listed, give the best results, and save a lot of time.

To find a lamp, two things must be known: the candlepower needed to produce the footcandle level at a given distance, and the spacing desired. The candlepower is determined by using the Inverse Square Law and the spacing, discussed in Chapter 3, is determined by the beam angle.

The next step is to search a lamp specification sheet for a lamp having both the candlepower and the beam angle desired.

Example:

The room is a kitchen that requires an adjusted Fc level of 50. The ceiling height is 96 inches and the counter is standard at 36 inches. The lighting will be recessed, using directional incandescent or halogen lamps.

Employing the Inverse Square Law, the candlepower for general lighting is determined to be 1,250. Don't be surprised if you can't find a lamp with exactly the Cp you are looking for. Try to come within a range plus or minus 15%. If possible, it is better to err on the side of more rather than less light. A dimmer can be utilized to bring the lighting level down a bit without adversely affecting the color temperature.

As to spacing and the beam angle, I usually look for lamps between 40° to 60° for a kitchen with an 8 foot ceiling; preferring 50° to 60°. In looking at the Spacing Table in Chapter 3, 40° to 60° will have a spacing of 39 inches to 62 inches with a 6 - inch intersect above the counter (workplane). Spacing at 39 inches is a little tight, but will work. As the lamps get closer together, the ceiling will take on a Swiss cheese appearance.

I will confine my search to halogen lamps due to the preferred color temperature between 2,900k to 3,200k. For general lighting, low-voltage lamps are not recommended due to the higher cost. On occasion, however, the smaller physical size of MR16 cans, for example, may make them the only choice. There are always many factors to consider that vary from project to project.

Searching *Appendix A* for lamps in the above ranges, the following are candidates for the project:

GE 60W PAR 38/HIR/WFL 1250 Cp 53°

Phillips 50W PAR30/HAL/FL40 1250 Cp 40°

Sylvania 50W PAR 30/CAPFL40 1300 Cp 40°

There are more choices, but these will be adequate for this discussion.

The first two lamps from GE and Phillips are right on at 1250 Cp, while the Sylvania is a little higher at 1300 Cp. By using the formula solving for Fc, the Sylvania lamp is shown to produce 52 Fc; certainly acceptable.

The deciding factors among these three lamps are availability, the various spacing, and appearance. Some designers are limited to certain lines. The 53° beam angle will be spaced at approximately 54 inches with the 40° lamps at 39 inches. The PAR30s are smaller and will tuck into the trim a bit higher than the PAR38.

The important thing is that you are in control, all the while knowing whichever lamp you decide upon will provide the necessary illumination at the spacing you dictate based on preference and architectural limitations.

Finding lamps for task lighting will be done the same way as the previous example, altering the candlepower and beam angle to fit the task surface being illuminated. Low voltage lamps, specifically MR16 lamps, are ideal for this purpose due to their variety of beam angles and candlepower.

Using the Candlepower Table

If you are one of those people who hate math, I have included a real time saver for finding the candlepower necessary to provide the workplane with any footcandle level at any distance. The candlepower Table, figure 4.6, on the following page is as close to effortless as it gets.

Based on the Inverse Square Law formula, which solves for unknown candlepower, the Table allows the designer to quickly locate the needed candlepower.

This is how it works:

If the room in question is a bathroom and it has been determined that the desired footcandle level is 30, and the lighting will be recessed cans in an 84-inch height soffit over a 30-inch vanity, all the information to use the table is known.

Note that across the top of the table are listed various Fc levels. Down the left side are listed various distances in feet.

Remember that distance is always measured in feet. Convert the soffit and vanity height to feet, 7 feet and 2.5 feet respectively. Subtracting the vanity height from the soffit height will yield the distance, 4.5 feet.

First, read across the uppermost row until you find 30 Fc. This is atop the column that you will now look down. Follow this column down to the row labeled 4.5 feet. Where the 30 Fc column and the 4.5 foot row intersect will be the 608 candlepower needed.

If the project is a kitchen with desired Fc levels for general at 40 and task at 100, and the 8 foot ceiling will have recessed cans, the process is the same.

Find the Distance by subtracting the counter height (3 feet) from the ceiling height (8 feet) which equals 5 feet.

Follow the top row across to 40 Fc and down that column to the 5-foot row to discover the Cp is 1,000. This is for general.

For task, follow the top row across to 100 Fc and down that column to the 5-foot row to find the 2,500 Cp needed.

It's a lot like letting your fingers do the walking.

What if the Fc is Not Listed

The table lists Fc levels up to 100. It is also possible to use the table for **any** Fc level above 100.

The following example will yield the candlepower necessary to provide 133 Fc at a distance of 3 feet.

Break 133 into its three unit columns', in other words, ones, tens, and hundreds (remember elementary school). There are 3 one's, 1 thirty, and 1 hundred. The solution is to find the Cp level for each and then total them.

Travel across the 3-foot row to the 100 Fc column to find 900 Cp. In the same 3-foot row, find the Cp for the 30 Fc column (270 Cp) and the 1 Fc Column (9 Cp).

3 @ 9	=	27
1 @ 270	=	270
1 @ 900	=	900
		1,197 Cp

A very cool table... as tables go!!

Candlepower Table

Use this table to determine the lamp candlepower necessary to provide the desired footcandle level at a known distance above the workplane.

Footcandle Level — Candlepower

Distance to Workplane	1Fc	5Fc	10Fc	15Fc	20Fc	25Fc	30Fc	35Fc	40Fc	45Fc	50Fc	55Fc	60Fc	65Fc	70Fc	75Fc	80Fc	85Fc	90Fc	95Fc	100Fc
0.5'	.3	1	3	4	5	6	8	9	10	11	13	14	15	16	18	19	20	21	23	24	25
1'	1	5	10	15	20	25	30	35	40	45	50	55	60	65	70	75	80	85	90	95	100
1.5'	2	11	23	34	45	56	68	79	90	101	113	124	135	146	158	169	180	191	203	214	225
1.75'	3	15	31	46	61	77	92	107	123	138	153	168	184	199	214	230	245	260	276	291	306
2'	4	20	40	60	80	100	120	140	160	180	200	220	240	260	280	300	320	340	360	380	400
2.25'	5	25	51	76	101	127	152	177	203	228	253	278	304	329	354	380	405	430	456	481	506
2.5'	6	31	63	94	125	156	188	219	250	281	313	344	375	406	438	469	500	531	563	594	625
2.75'	8	38	76	113	151	189	227	265	303	340	378	416	454	492	529	567	605	643	681	718	756
3'	9	45	90	135	180	225	270	315	360	405	450	495	540	585	630	675	720	765	810	855	900
3.5'	12	61	123	184	245	306	368	429	490	551	613	674	735	796	858	919	980	1,041	1,103	1,164	1,225
4'	16	80	160	240	320	400	480	560	640	720	800	880	960	1,040	1,120	1,200	1,280	1,360	1,440	1,520	1,600
4.5'	20	101	203	304	405	506	608	709	810	911	1,013	1,114	1,215	1,316	1,418	1,519	1,620	1,721	1,823	1,924	2,025
5'	25	125	250	375	500	625	750	875	1,000	1,125	1,250	1,375	1,500	1,625	1,750	1,875	2,000	2,125	2,250	2,375	2,500
5.5'	30	151	303	454	605	756	908	1,059	1,210	1,361	1,513	1,664	1,815	1,966	2,118	2,269	2,420	2,571	2,723	2,874	3,025
6'	36	180	360	540	720	900	1,080	1,260	1,440	1,620	1,800	1,980	2,160	2,340	2,520	2,700	2,880	3,060	3,240	3,420	3,600
6.5'	42	211	423	634	845	1,056	1,268	1,479	1,690	1,901	2,113	2,324	2,535	2,746	2,958	3,169	3,380	3,591	3,803	4,014	4,225
7'	49	245	490	735	980	1,225	1,470	1,715	1,960	2,205	2,450	2,695	2,940	3,185	3,430	3,675	3,920	4,165	4,410	4,655	4,900
7.5'	56	281	563	844	1,125	1,406	1,688	1,969	2,250	2,531	2,813	3,094	3,375	3,656	3,938	4,219	4,500	4,781	5,063	5,344	5,625
8'	64	320	640	960	1,280	1,600	1,920	2,240	2,560	2,880	3,200	3,520	3,840	4,160	4,480	4,800	5,120	5,440	5,760	6,080	6,400
8.5'	72	361	723	1,084	1,445	1,806	2,168	2,529	2,890	3,251	3,613	3,974	4,335	4,696	5,058	5,419	5,780	6,141	6,503	6,864	7,225
9'	81	405	810	1,215	1,620	2,025	2,430	2,835	3,240	3,645	4,050	4,455	4,860	5,265	5,670	6,075	6,480	6,885	7,290	7,695	8,100
9.5'	90	451	903	1,354	1,805	2,256	2,708	3,159	3,610	4,061	4,513	4,964	5,415	5,866	6,318	6,769	7,220	7,671	8,123	8,574	9,025
10'	100	500	1,000	1,500	2,000	2,500	3,000	3,500	4,000	4,500	5,000	5,500	6,000	6,500	7,000	7,500	8,000	8,500	9,000	9,500	10,000

Figure 4.6

Putting Spacing and the CandlePower Table Together

It is time to revisit the island, Figure 3.16, from Chapter 3 as promised. We used the Spacing Table to determine the appropriate spacing and beam angle to adequately cover the island with light. It is now time to go through the process of finding a candlepower that will provide the necessary footcandle level. Once this is done, we can search through *Appendix A* to find a lamp.

In Chapter 3, the beam angle for Figure 3.16, now 4.7 was found to be 60°, the distance was established at 27 inches (2.25'). Now let's use the candlepower table, figure 4.6, to find the Cp the lamp needs to be to provide the "rule-of-the-road" 100 Fc Task illumination level.

Travel down the distance row to 2.25' (27 inches) and across to the 100 Fc column. At the intersection you will find 506 Cp. At the 27 inch distance, it will require a lamp with 506 Cp to provide 100 Fc to the island surface.

It was also decided in Chapter 3 that an MR16 was to be used. We now have all the information needed to search *Appendix A* for an MR16 lamp to specify for our pendant fixture.

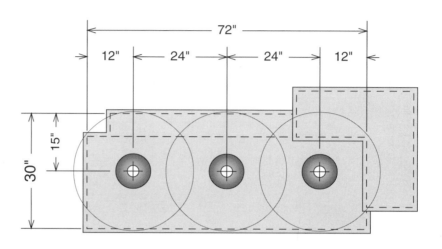

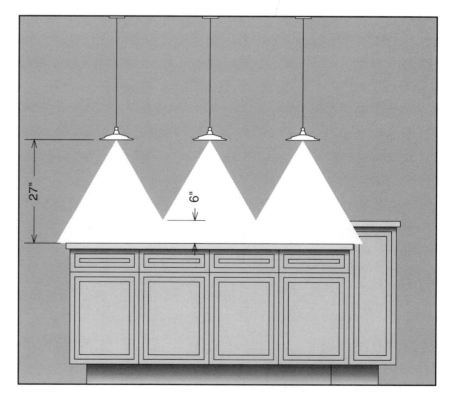

Figure 4.7   **Task lighting at an island**

Go to *Appendix A* and search for MR16 lamps in the "Halogen Low Voltage" section for lamps around 506 Cp and with a 60° beam angle. Remember, you will probably not find an exact match, but you do know an ideal to search for.

My search came up with only one candidate:

Page 165		650	Cp
Syl 35MR16Q/60°/VWFL/T/C		60°	Beam°

Now all you have to do is find a pendant that will complement the motif of the room and handle the wattage of the lamp. Most pendants will handle at least 50 watts, but always make sure to check the specifications of the fixture. That is about all there is to it.

The Lumen Method

The Lumen Method is a formula which allows the designer to determine the proper number of luminaires (i.e., lamp, trim, and fixture) to maintain the desired footcandle level in a room. It can be used with any luminaire for which the fixture manufacturer has provided a CU (coefficient of utilization) table. The CU table simply gives the percentage of the light produced by a luminaire (fixture, trim, and lamp), which actually gets down to the workplane. CU tables for fluorescent luminaires are more readily available than for incandescent. Most manufacturers are providing CU tables in all their literature covering the newer compact fluorescent luminaires.

While the Inverse Square Law works well with lamps that produce their own cone of light (beam angle), it won't work for lamps that, by themselves, do not produce a beam angle. Omni-directional lamps, such as linear fluorescent tubes and compact fluorescents, do not produce their own cone of light, but instead rely on the fixture and the fixture trim to redirect the light into the room, creating the cone. Since candlepower is a product of the focused intensity of the lamp, there is no candlepower associated with a lamp that doesn't produce a cone. There is still a need, however, to determine the number of lamps, or more specifically, the number of luminaires necessary to provide the proper amount of illumination to the space. This is where the Lumen Method comes in.

The Lumen Method can be used with any lamp, incandescent or fluorescent, directional or omni-directional that the manufacturer has placed in a fixture and tested to find how much light actually reaches the workplane. The results of this testing is published in the form of a CU table.

Here is the rub. Not all fixtures and lamps are tested in combination. A manufacturer may elect to test one compact fluorescent lamp in a recessed can and ignore testing a halogen PAR lamp altogether. ***Without a CU table, the Lumen Method is worthless.*** It is for this reason that the Inverse Square Law has been included in this book.

On the following page is a worksheet for doing the Lumen Method calculations. At the bottom of the sheet is a formula that will also provide the proper spacing for the luminaire to produce evenly the desired Fc level in the room. Use this sheet as a master for reproducing worksheets for your office.

The best way to explain the use of the worksheet is to go through an example. As you can see, Steps 1 through 5 culminate in finding the CU percentage from a table. It is a good time then to learn how to read one before proceeding to the Lumen Method explanation.

Lumen Method Calculation Sheet

Project Name: _____
Fixture Manufacturer: _____
Model Number: _____
Room Length: _____ ft.   Room Width: _____ ft.
Lamp Type: _____
Color Temperature: _____   CRI: _____
Lamps per Fixture: _____   Lumens per Lamp: _____
Total Fixture Lumens: _____
Desired Footcandle Level: _____

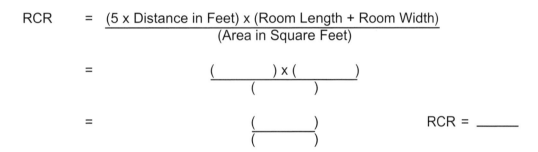

Ceiling Reflectance (CCR)
Wall Reflectance (WCR)
Distance
W O R K P L A N E
Floor Reflectance (FCR)

Step 1: Determine RCR (Room Cavity Ratio):

$$\text{RCR} \quad = \quad \frac{(5 \times \text{Distance in Feet}) \times (\text{Room Length} + \text{Room Width})}{(\text{Area in Square Feet})}$$

$$= \quad \frac{(\quad\quad) \times (\quad\quad)}{(\quad\quad)}$$

$$= \quad \frac{(\quad\quad)}{(\quad\quad)} \qquad\qquad \text{RCR} = \underline{\quad\quad}$$

Step 2: CCR _____ ~ *use 80% if ceiling reflectance is unknown.*
Step 3: WCR _____ ~ *use 50% if wall reflectance is unknown.*
Step 4: FCR _____ ~ *use 20% if floor reflectance is unknown.*
Step 5: **CU**: _____ ~ *use the info from steps 1-4 to obtain CU from a manufacturers' table.*
Step 6: LLF: _____ ~ *use 75% as a rule of thumb. (Light Loss Factor)*
Step 7: Number of Fixtures:

$$= \quad \frac{(\text{Footcandle Level}) \times (\text{Area in Square Feet})}{(\text{Total Fixture Lumens}) \times (\textbf{CU}) \times (\text{LLF})}$$

$$= \quad \frac{(\quad\quad) \times (\quad\quad)}{(\quad\quad) \times (\quad\quad) \times (\quad\quad)}$$

$$= \quad \frac{(\quad\quad)}{(\quad\quad)} \qquad \text{Number of Fixtures} = \underline{\quad\quad}$$

Step 8: Fixture Spacing:

$$= \quad \sqrt{\frac{(\text{Total Fixture Lumens}) \times (\textbf{CU}) \times (\text{LLF})}{(\text{Footcandle Level})}}$$

$$= \quad \sqrt{\frac{(\quad\quad) \times (\quad\quad) \times (\quad\quad)}{(\quad\quad)}}$$

$$= \quad \sqrt{\frac{(\quad\quad)}{(\quad\quad)}} \qquad \text{Fixture Spacing} = \underline{\quad\quad} \text{ ft.}$$

CU Tables *(Coefficient of Utilization)*

Coefficient of Utilization (CU) tables, just by their name, sound technically intimidating. They are really quite friendly and, when made available by a fixture manufacturer, provide necessary information about luminaires. A luminaire is the combination of a fixture, its trim, and a lamp. Remember, while a directional lamp produces its own cone of light, an omni-directional lamp must rely on the fixture and its trim to produce the cone and therefore has no candlepower rating. It is for this reason that the Inverse Square Law can't be used for omni-directional lamps. However, if a fixture manufacturer provides a CU table for a luminaire using a directional lamp, the Lumen Method can be used instead of the Inverse Square Law; both provide accurate results.

A CU table lists the amount of light from a luminaire which actually reaches the workplane. It is expressed as a percentage. For example, if a value from a CU table is .50, then 50% of the light the luminaire produces actually makes it to the workplane. The CU percentage is necessary to use the Lumen Method. Also, the CU table takes into account the reflectance levels in the room.

Reading a CU Table

In order to find a luminaires' efficiency for a room being designed, you must know the shape of the room, the colors used in the space, and the distance the lamps are from the workplane.

Lighting engineers, in their usual manner of making things seem more difficult than they should be, have devised a way of defining the shape of the room and the distance the lamp is above the workplane as a whole number from 1 to 10. They call this number the RCR (Room Cavity Ratio). Again, a tactic to put the fear of the ancients into our very soul.

Finding the RCR

To arrive at the RCR you must plug the length and width of the room (in feet) and the distance (also in feet) into the formula below. As an example, lets' use a room that is 15 feet in length, 10 feet in width, and where the lamp or luminaire will be 5 feet above the workplane. Plug the information into the formula and do the calculations. The first 5 in the formula is a constant; in other words, always a 5.

$$RCR = \frac{(5 \times Distance) \times (Length + Width)}{(Area)}$$

$$= \frac{(5 \times 5') \times (15' + 10')}{(15' \times 10')}$$

$$= \frac{25 \times 25}{150}$$

$$= \frac{625}{150}$$

$$= 4$$

Believe it or not, the engineers say this room has a RCR of 4. Always round to the nearest whole number.

Figure 4.8 demonstrates how the RCR is used to determine the CU of a luminaire.

Using RCR and Reflectance to determine a luminaires' CU

Building on the example from the previous page, let's also assume that the example room has a white ceiling with a reflectance of 80%, and an average wall reflectance of 50%. The floor reflectance does not come into play as yet. Figure 4.8 will use this new information as it explains how to derive the CU percentage from a CU table.

The table has been *exploded* for visual clarity.

The first step is to decide where in the table to look. The table is broken into four major blocks (80%, 70%, 50%, 30%) which indicate the ceiling reflectance (CCR).

In our example, the ceiling is white which is usually considered 80%. The block labeled 80% has been pulled forward. The rest of your search will be confined to this block.

The next step is to find the proper vertical column within the 80% block found in step 1. The block is broken into vertical columns by average wall reflectance (WCR).

In our example, the average wall reflectance is 50%. The vertical column labeled 50% has been pulled forward. The rest of your search will be confined to this column.

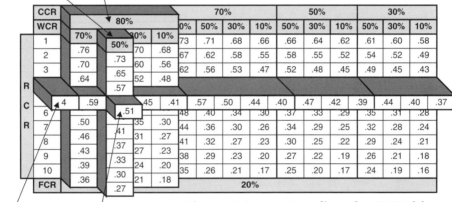

Figure 4.8   Reading the CU Table

The RCR indicates the room shape and distance. There are always 10 horizontal RCR rows numbered from 1 to 10. You must now decide which row to look in.

In our example, the 10' x 15' room with a distance of 5' had a RCR of 4. Row 4 has been pulled forward. The rest of your search will be confined to this row.

You will find, where the vertical (WCR) column and the horizontal (RCR) row intersect, the CU percentage or efficiency of the luminaire (.51). In other words, 51% of the light generated by the luminaire actually reaches the workplane.

It is this CU percentage that is used in the Lumen Method Calculation Sheet explained in Chapter 4.

Working through the Lumen Method Worksheet

The example scenario for this worksheet will be the following: Kitchen general lighting with a desired Fc level of 40. The room is 9 feet wide and 13 feet long with a 9 foot ceiling. This will make the distance 6 feet. The reflectance levels are ceiling (80%), average walls (50%), and floor (20%).

Any fixture can be tested when there is a CU table for it. *Appendix B* lists several CU tables for consideration. Let's do the first table listed, Table A, for this discussion. Using the information found within CU Table A, we will fill out the worksheet on the following page. Start at the top and work your way to the bottom.

Identify the project as "Table A". *(from the CU table)*
Normally something like, "Jones Kitchen."

Fill in the fixture manufacturer. *(from the CU table)*

Fill in the fixture model no. *(from the CU table)*

Note room length and width.
(from the description at left)

Fill in the lamp type. *(from the CU table)*

Fill in the lamp Color Temperature and CRI.
Cool White lamps are usually about 4,200k/62 CRI.
These numbers do not enter into the calculations, but are important to consider.
(chapter 2 or appendix A)

Note the number of lamps used in the luminaire.
(from the CU table)

Note the Lumen rating of each lamp.
(from the CU table)

Multiply the Lumen value by the number of lamps.

Note the desired Footcandle level. *(this chapter)*

Step 1: Calculate the RCR that describes the room shape as a whole number between 1 and 10. The first number in the formula is a constant (5); in other words, always a 5.
(see explanation in Appendix B)

Step 2: fill in the 80% color reflectance.
(from the description at left)

Step 3: fill in the 50% average wall reflectance.
(from the description at left)

Step 4: fill in the 20% floor reflectance.
(from the description at left)

Step 5: find the CU in Table A.
(see explanation in Appendix B)

Step 6: Use 75%
A lamp used in a residential setting loses, on the average, about 25% of its brilliance (intensity) over the life of the lamp. LLF in the formula takes this eventual loss into account.

Step 7: Using the information you have already entered into the worksheet above, plug the requested information into the formula and perform the calculations to find the number of luminaires necessary to provide the desired Fc level.

Step 8: Again, using the information you have already entered into the worksheet above, plug the requested information into the formula and perform the calculations to find the Spacing between luminaires to maintain the desired Fc level evenly throughout the room.

Note: the two shaded areas in steps 7 and 8 are the same number. Once you have determined the number in the shaded area in step 7, simply copy it to the shaded area in step 8.

Lumen Method Calculation Sheet

Project Name: _CU Table A ---Kitchen---_
Fixture Manufacturer: _Lithonia_
Model Number: _LB 240A_
Room Length: _13'_ ft.   Room Width: _9'_ ft.
Lamp Type: _F40T12 CW_
Color Temperature: _~ 4,200k_ _yuk!_   CRI: _62_ _yuk!_
Lamps per Fixture: _2_   Lumens per Lamp: _2,650_
Total Fixture Lumens: _5,300_
Desired FootCandle Level: _40 Fc_

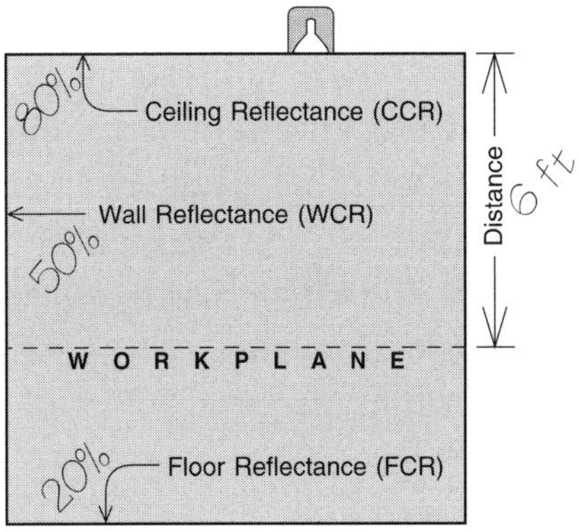

Ceiling Reflectance (CCR) _80%_
Wall Reflectance (WCR) _50%_
W O R K P L A N E
Floor Reflectance (FCR) _20%_
Distance _6 ft_

Step 1: Determine RCR (Room Cavity Ratio):

$$RCR = \frac{(5 \times \text{Distance in Feet}) \times (\text{Room Length} + \text{Room Width})}{(\text{Area in Square Feet})}$$

_6_   _13'_   _9'_

$$= \frac{(\ 30' \ ) \times (\ 22' \ )}{(117 \text{ sq. ft.})}$$

round to the nearest whole number... 6

$$= \frac{(\ 660 \ )}{(\ 117 \ )}$$ RCR = _5.6_

Step 2: CCR _.80_ ~ use 80% if ceiling reflectance is unknown.
Step 3: WCR _.50_ ~ use 50% if wall reflectance is unknown.
Step 4: FCR _.20_ ~ use 20% if floor reflectance is unknown.
Step 5: **CU**: _.41_ ~ use the info from steps 1-4 to obtain CU from a manufacturers' table.
Step 6: LLF: _.75_ ~ use 75% as a rule of thumb. (Light Loss Factor)
Step 7: Number of Fixtures:

$$= \frac{(\text{FootCandle Level}) \times (\text{Area in Square Feet})}{(\text{Total Fixture Lumens}) \times (\textbf{CU}) \times (\text{LLF})}$$

$$= \frac{(\ 40 \text{ Fc} \ ) \times (117 \text{ sq. ft.})}{(\ 5,300 \ ) \times (\ .41 \text{ CU} \ ) \times (\ .75 \text{ LLF} \ )}$$

round to the nearest whole fixture... 3

$$= \frac{(\ 4,680 \ )}{(\ 1,630 \ )}$$ Number of Fixtures = _2.87_

Step 8: Fixture Spacing:

$$= \sqrt{\frac{(\text{Total Fixture Lumens}) \times (\textbf{CU}) \times (\text{LLF})}{(\text{FootCandle Level})}}$$

$$= \sqrt{\frac{(\ 5,300 \ ) \times (\ .41 \text{ CU} \ ) \times (\ .75 \text{ LLF} \ )}{(\ 40 \text{ Fc} \ )}}$$

_or 77"_

$$= \sqrt{\frac{(\ 1,630 \ )}{(\ 40 \text{ Fc} \ )}}$$ Fixture Spacing = _6.38_ ft.

Figure 4.9

The results of the Lumen Method for the example kitchen in figure 4.9, using the fluorescent luminaire described in CU Table A, are that it will take 2.87 fixtures (rounded to 3), spaced 77 inches center to center to provide the kitchen with 40 Fc of general illumination to the workplane 6 feet below the fixture.

Relamping the Fixture

The Cool White lamp in the previous example is of very poor color quality. The question now becomes: what if you would rather use a lamp that doesn't destroy the colors of the interior decor *and* you can't find a CU Table for the fixture with a higher caliber lamp?

All that is necessary is to exchange the lumen value in the worksheet for the lumen value of the lamp you would like to use.

Drawing on what we learned from Chapter 2 on color temperature and CRI, it is preferable to use a lamp that is between 2,900k - 3,500k with a CRI over 80. In scanning *Appendix A* for a 4 foot linear fluorescent tube (F40T12), several candidates are found:

Page 170	2,900 Lumens
GE F40SPX35/RS/WM	82 CRI 3500k
Page 172	2,900 Lumens
Phil F40/35U/RS/EW	85 CRI 3500k
Page 174	2,900 Lumens
Syl F40/D835/SS	80 CRI 3500k

Notice how easy it was to locate these three lamps using the Ⓔ ☺ *symbols.*

The three lamps represent the total offering from the three major manufacturers which comply with the guidelines set forth in Chapter 2. Stop and think about all the lamps offered on the market of the F40T12 type. Using lamps of this order will give the best, most efficient results and, in the long run, will be less expensive than the cheaper lamps which seem to proliferate.

On the next page, the Lumen Method calculation worksheet is identical to the worksheet on the previous page except that the lumen value has been changed. The lumen value from the CU table, 2,650, has been replaced by the lumen value of any of the three newly found lamps, 2,900.

The results, then, of the recalculated worksheet are that it will take 2.62 fixtures (rounded to 3), spaced 80 inches center to center to provide the kitchen with 40 Fc of general illumination to the workplane 6 feet below the fixture. The same number of fixtures, in this case, will be needed and about the same spacing.

It is acceptable to do the exchange of lumens from one lamp to another as long as it is the same type of lamp. PAR 30 for a PAR 30 or R30 for a R30. Don't exchange a PAR 30 for a R30, however.

If this seems laborious, lighting software is available to instantly perform these calculations. See the back of this book for further information.

Lumen Method Calculation Sheet

Project Name: _CU Table A ---Kitchen---_
Fixture Manufacturer: _Lithonia_   _ALTERNATE LAMP_
Model Number: _LB 240A_
Room Length: _13'_ ft.   Room Width: _9'_ ft.
Lamp Type: _F40SPX35_
Color Temperature: _~3,500k_ _yes!_   CRI: _82_ _yes!_
Lamps per Fixture: _2_   Lumens per Lamp: _2,900_
Total Fixture Lumens: _5,800_
Desired Footcandle Level: _40 Fc_

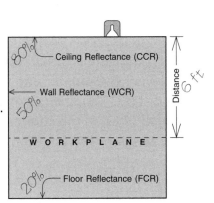

Step 1: Determine RCR (Room Cavity Ratio):

$$RCR = \frac{(5 \times \text{Distance in Feet}) \times (\text{Room Length} + \text{Room Width})}{(\text{Area in Square Feet})}$$

(6')   (13')   (9')

$$= \frac{(\ 30'\ ) \times (\ 22'\ )}{(117 \text{ sq. ft.})}$$

$$= \frac{(\ 660\ )}{(\ 117\ )}$$ *round to the nearest whole number ... 6*   RCR = _5.6_

Step 2: CCR _.80_ ~ use 80% if ceiling reflectance is unknown.
Step 3: WCR _.50_ ~ use 50% if wall reflectance is unknown.
Step 4: FCR _.20_ ~ use 20% if floor reflectance is unknown.
Step 5: **CU**: _.41_ ~ use the info from steps 1-4 to obtain CU from a manufacturers' table.
Step 6: LLF: _.75_ ~ use 75% as a rule of thumb. (Light Loss Factor)
Step 7: Number of Fixtures:

$$= \frac{(\text{Footcandle Level}) \times (\text{Area in Square Feet})}{(\text{Total Fixture Lumens}) \times (\textbf{CU}) \times (\text{LLF})}$$

$$= \frac{(\ 40 \text{ Fc}\ ) \times (117 \text{ sq. ft.})}{(\ 5,800\ ) \times (\ .41 \text{ CU}\ ) \times (\ .75 \text{ LLF}\ )}$$ *round to the nearest whole fixture ... 3*

$$= \frac{(\ 4,680\ )}{(\ 1,784\ )}$$ Number of Fixtures = _2.62_

Step 8: Fixture Spacing:

$$= \sqrt{\frac{(\text{Total Fixture Lumens}) \times (\textbf{CU}) \times (\text{LLF})}{(\text{Footcandle Level})}}$$

$$= \sqrt{\frac{(\ 5,800\ ) \times (\ .41 \text{ CU}\ ) \times (\ .75 \text{ LLF}\ )}{(\ 40 \text{ Fc}\ )}}$$ *or 80'*

$$= \sqrt{\frac{(\ 1,784\ )}{(\ 40 \text{ Fc}\ )}}$$ Fixture Spacing = _6.68_ ft.

Figure 4.10

Some Final Thoughts

Through the tools presented in this Chapter it is possible to calculate the footcandle level necessary for any residential setting or task. Whether planning to use directional or omni-directional lamps, the lighting designer can achieve the footcandle level using either the Inverse Square Law or the lumen method. If the fixture manufacturer has provided a CU table, the lumen method can be used, if not and the lamp is directional, the Inverse Square Law can be used. Using either method, in conjunction with the lamp information provided in *Appendix A* and the CU tables in *Appendix B*, the number of luminaires and the best lamp for the job can be specified. Much better than rule-of-thumb approaches, your results will be accurate and repeatable from project to project.

In Chapter 6 we will put together all that we have learned in realistic kitchen and bath examples. Before doing that, a look at lamps and fixtures in Chapter 5 will offer additional insights into the variety of lamp technologies and fixture configurations.

Rules of the Road

Even though I recommend against using rules-of-thumb, there are some ways to *reuse* information in your lighting projects.

If a particular lamp is found to work well for general or task lighting in a bath or a kitchen at a given distance, its performance can be duplicated in other similar kitchens and baths. Once found, a log can be kept of various scenarios (lamp, luminaire, room function, room size, distance, reflectance, etc.) as a reference for future jobs.

Included with the CU tables in *Appendix B* is a fixture per square foot rating; all for a specific room size and room reflectance. This rating can be multiplied by rooms of various sizes to quickly arrive at a fixture count. Obviously, if the room shape varies greatly, the factor will need to be changed. However, within a range, the factor will hold true. For the luminaires that you use and that your distributor carries, determine a factor that can be used to save time with good results.

Why not just give you my solutions for various situations? Because my sense of design, taste, experience will be different than every person who reads this book; not better or worse, just different. Design is an expression and by understanding the tools of lighting calculation, the designer will be better able to achieve his or her own vision within a set of reliable recommendations from the IES.

QUIZ

1. The first step in performing lighting calculations is to establish the footcandle level for the room and the activities that will occur within it?

   T   F

2. What is the base footcandle level for general lighting in a Bath _____? Kitchen _____? Task lighting in a kitchen _____?

3. For a bathroom with a "dark" average reflectance and a black granite counter surface, what is the adjusted footcandle level for general lighting?
   - a.) 30 Fc
   - b.) 53 Fc
   - c.) 71 Fc
   - d.) 133 Fc

4. When the colors of a room are not known, what is the task lighting Fc level for an island in a kitchen?
   - a.) 53 Fc
   - b.) 71 Fc
   - c.) 100 Fc
   - d.) 133 Fc

5. Art lighting should be _____ times brighter than the surrounding light level?
   - a.) 2
   - b.) 5
   - c.) 8
   - d.) Should be the same as the ambient light level of the room.

6. The Inverse Square Law can be used for _____ only?
   - a.) omni-directional lamps
   - b.) directional lamps
   - c.) bi-lateral lamps
   - d.) equatorial lamps

7. What is the candlepower needed for a lamp mounted 60 inches above an island which will require 100 Fc?
   - a.) 1250 Cp
   - b.) 1725 Cp
   - c.) 2500 Cp
   - d.) 4375 Cp

   Use the candlepower Table, Figure 4.6, for question 8.

8. If a lamp is to be mounted at 27 inches above an island counter, what will the Cp of the lamp need to be to provide 175 Fc?

   _____ Cp

9. Using the same lamp across a vaulted ceiling will _____ ?
   - a.) be very uplifting.
   - b.) result in a lower Fc level as the Distance to the lamp increases across the vault.
   - c.) void the warranty of the highest lamp.
   - d.) will change the beam angle of the lamp.

10. If a 1400 Cp lamp is to be used in a pendant. At what distance will it produce 133 Fc on the workplane?

_____ "

11. What Fc level is on a surface 48" below a lamp rated at 900 Cp?

_____ Fc

12. If the distance remains the same, as the candlepower increases, so does the Fc level?
T   F

13. In looking for a directional lamp, what two things must be considered for an evenly distributed field of light?
a.)   CRI and Distance
b.)   Matter and Anti-Matter
c.)   Beam Angle and Candlepower
d.)   Candlepower and Impulse Power

14. The Lumen Method can be used for any luminaire?
T   F

15. If a CU table is not available, but the luminaire is virtually identical to one of the listed CU tables in *Appendix B*, it is permissible to use the table in *Appendix B* for the Lumen Method calculation?
T   F

16. The CU table measures the percentage of light from a luminaire that actually reaches the workplane?
T   F

17. The Lumen Method Calculation Worksheet can be used to find the number of luminaires and their beam angles?
T   F

Use the Lumen Method Calculation Worksheet to do question 18.

18. In an 11 foot by 12 foot kitchen with a ceiling height of 8 feet, determine the number of recessed fixtures needed for general lighting and the spacing using the luminaire described in Appendix B/ Table G. The kitchen has an 80% reflective ceiling, 70% walls, 20% counters, and 20% floor. You will need to calculate the Fc level as well to complete the problem?

19. What is the per square foot factor for this lamp?

_____ fixtures per Sq. Ft.

Lumen Method Calculation Sheet

Project Name: _____

Fixture Manufacturer: _____

Model Number: _____

Room Length: _____ ft.   Room Width: _____ ft.

Lamp Type: _____

Color Temperature: _____   CRI: _____

Lamps per Fixture: _____   Lumens per Lamp: _____

Total Fixture Lumens: _____

Desired Footcandle Level: _____

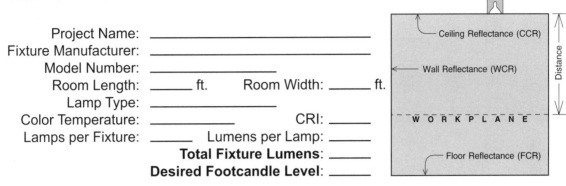

Step 1: Determine RCR (Room Cavity Ratio):

$$RCR = \frac{(5 \times \text{Distance in Feet}) \times (\text{Room Length} + \text{Room Width})}{(\text{Area in Square Feet})}$$

$$= \frac{(\underline{\quad}) \times (\underline{\quad})}{(\underline{\quad})}$$

$$= \frac{(\underline{\quad})}{(\underline{\quad})} \qquad RCR = \underline{\quad}$$

Step 2: CCR _____ ~ *use 80% if ceiling reflectance is unknown.*

Step 3: WCR _____ ~ *use 50% if wall reflectance is unknown.*

Step 4: FCR _____ ~ *use 20% if floor reflectance is unknown.*

Step 5: **CU**: _____ ~ *use the info from steps 1-4 to obtain CU from a manufacturers' table.*

Step 6: LLF: _____ ~ *use 75% as a rule of thumb. (Light Loss Factor)*

Step 7: Number of Fixtures:

$$= \frac{(\text{Footcandle Level}) \times (\text{Area in Square Feet})}{(\text{Total Fixture Lumens}) \times (\textbf{CU}) \times (\text{LLF})}$$

$$= \frac{(\underline{\quad}) \times (\underline{\quad})}{(\underline{\quad}) \times (\underline{\quad}) \times (\underline{\quad})}$$

$$= \frac{(\underline{\quad})}{(\underline{\quad})} \qquad \text{Number of Fixtures} = \underline{\quad}$$

Step 8: Fixture Spacing:

$$= \sqrt{\frac{(\text{Total Fixture Lumens}) \times (\textbf{CU}) \times (\text{LLF})}{(\text{Footcandle Level})}}$$

$$= \sqrt{\frac{(\underline{\quad}) \times (\underline{\quad}) \times (\underline{\quad})}{(\underline{\quad})}}$$

$$= \sqrt{\frac{(\underline{\quad})}{(\underline{\quad})}} \qquad \text{Fixture Spacing} = \underline{\quad} \text{ ft.}$$

CHAPTER 5

LAMPS & FIXTURES

Incandescent, Halogen, Fluorescent, and Compact Fluorescent all describe current technologies used in the manufacture of lamps for the residential market. These lamps come in a myriad of shapes which gives rise to the seeming limitless variety of fixtures to house and direct the light output.

In this Chapter, we will discuss:

- **Major Lamp Technologies**

  - Incandescent

  - Halogen

  - Fluorescent

  - Compact Fluorescent

- **Fixtures**

  - Recessed Line Voltage

  - Recessed Low Voltage

  - Track

  - Accessories

In Chapters 1 - 4 we learned about the quality and amount of light needed for various rooms and activities. This knowledge coupled with some insights into the lamp technologies available and the fixtures which house them will complete the foundation of information needed to create a successful lighting plan for not only the kitchen or bath, but any room in the house.

Lamp Technologies

Incandescent

The oldest of the lamp design technologies, dating back to Edison, is incandescent. These lamps have changed little in the past 100 years and are still the most popular among homeowners today. A tungsten wire filament is placed inside a glass bulb, an electric current is passed through the filament and, through resistance, the filament heats and begins to glow or incandesce. "A" lamps and R (Reflector) lamps are the most common; both are line voltage.

The drawback to these lamps is that they are terribly inefficient and are decidedly in the warm color range. In fact, R lamps have been discontinued according to the federal energy efficiency laws known as EPACT. "A" lamps have been replaced with the somewhat more efficient TB or MB lamps and the R lamps have been replaced with the BR series. The color temperature of these new lamps is still quite warm (2,700k). All incandescent lamps provide a CRI of 100.

Whenever possible, find a suitable halogen or fluorescent substitute for these lamps.

Halogen

Halogen lamps are brighter, more efficient, and whiter (2,900k - 3,200k) than ordinary incandescent lamps while maintaining 100 CRI. By the way, halogen lamps are a special kind of incandescent. All halogen lamps are incandescent, but not all incandescent lamps are halogen.

The most common of the household halogen lamps are the line voltage PAR series lamps (PAR16, PAR20, PAR30, PAR38) and the low voltage MR series lamps (MR11, MR16) depicted in Figure 5.2. The MR lamps provide a much greater amount of light for its size than PAR lamps and allow excellent beam control. MR lamps are the preferred choice for task, accent, and art lighting while PAR lamps are used for everything from art and accent lighting to general lighting.

The technically *cool* thing about halogen lamps is that, unlike incandescent lamps where the tungsten filament literally evaporates into the lamp while converting 90% of the energy to heat *instead of light*, the halogen gas actually rebuilds or returns the evaporated tungsten to the filament which greatly increases the life and efficiency of the lamp.

Figure 5.1   *Popular Halogen Lamps*

GE & Phillips

Halogen Cycle

All halogen lamps feature a short, thick tungsten filament encased in a capsule filled with halogen gas. The regeneration cycle described below is the key to the long life and excellent maintenance of these lamps.

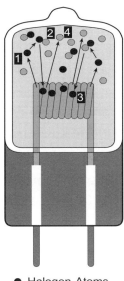

● Halogen Atoms

◎ Tungsten Atoms

1. Tungsten atoms evaporate from filament.
2. Tungsten atoms combine with halogen atoms.
3. Gaseous compound returns to hot filament, redepositing tungsten atoms.
4. Halogen atoms are released to combine with additional tungsten atoms.

Figure 5.2   **Halogen Cycle**   *Phillips*

The drawback to some halogen lamps is that, when they are dimmed, the halogen cycle is degraded which shortens the life of the lamp and may cause it to flicker. Some manufacturers say that when using dimmers, if the dimmer is raised to full power when the lamp is turned on and before it is turned off, the negative effects of dimming are reduced. Be aware, new halogen technologies are emerging which eliminate the problem all together. Check with your local lamp

representative about these lamps. Halogen lamps also maintain their brilliance over their life unlike fluorescent lamps which tend to fade by up to 25%.

Fluorescent

A fluorescent lamp is a "gaseous discharge" light source. Light is produced by passing an electric arc between tungsten cathodes at either end of a tube filled with a low pressure mercury vapor which generates radiant ultraviolet energy. This energy causes the phosphor coating on the inside of the tube to "fluoresce," converting the ultraviolet energy into visible light. A ballast is required to regulate the electrical current provided to the lamp. Some ballasts can be dimmed, but are quite expensive.

The various phosphor coatings available and the number of coatings dictate the energy efficiency of the lamp, its color temperature, and CRI. Fluorescent color issues have been covered in Chapter 2 and a more detailed explanation of the phosphor coatings is contained in the Glossary.

Fluorescent lamps are available from 2,700k to 6,500k and CRI ratings from 50 to 90. As stated in Chapter 2, *Color and Reflectance*, the best combination is 3,000k to 3,500k **and** over 80 CRI which is available in most tubular fluorescents.

Look for the T8 lamp to replace the T12 in the coming years. The T8 lamps are smaller in diameter, more energy efficient, and produce more light than their T12 counterparts.

Bottom line is that fluorescent is the most energy efficient light source for the home, for general lighting anyway. Fluorescent color technology has progressed to the point where there is little reason not to use it especially when considering the aesthetically pleasing recessed cans for the new compact fluorescent technology.

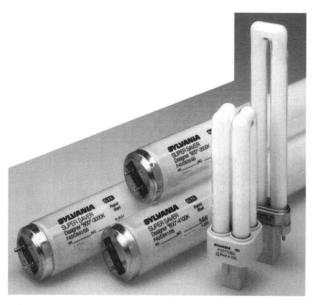

Figure 5.3   Fluorescent Lamps   *Sylvania*

Compact Fluorescent

The fastest growing application for fluorescent lamping today comes in the form of the compact fluorescent. These lamps feature a narrow tube that loops back on itself and attaches to a plastic base. The normal base is a pin mount which plugs into a fixture designed for it.

Screw bases with a built-in ballast are also available for replacing PAR and R lamps, but the added length of the ballast and screw mount often causes the lamp to protrude out of the can and below the ceiling line. Unfortunately, this has given a poor first impression of the lamp type to many designers. For a kitchen or bath, this single lamp retrofit is usually not powerful enough to provide the necessary footcandle level. Using the compact fluorescent horizontally in special recessed cans eliminates the problem and provides the best alternative for R and PAR lamps used for general lighting in the kitchen and bath. This fixture is covered later in the chapter.

Compact fluorescent lamps are available from 2,700k to 6,500k with a CRI rating over 80.

In California, the law dictates that fluorescent lighting shall be used for general lighting in the kitchen and bath. Using compact fluorescent lamps rated at 3,000k to 3,500k *and* 80 CRI in recessed cans for general lighting and halogen accent and task lighting in the form of MR16 or PAR lamps is, by far and away, the best combination for aesthetic effect and efficiency.

High Intensity Discharge

Stay away from all forms of this lighting for residential interiors. The lamps take several minutes to warm up (turn on) once they have been turned on. The color output from this lamp family is not suitable for residential interiors, and there are alleged safety concerns of residential HID use. These will not be covered in this publication.

Lamp Descriptions

MR16/MR11/MR16TAL Lamps

Compact halogen source, optically centered in a multi-faceted dichroic system, provides significant energy efficiency while reducing heat output. The TAL "Twist & Lock" base is also available. TAL and some other lamps have a covered lens, making them suitable for open fixtures.

20-75 Watts   2,000-5,000 Hours   Beam Angles: 7°-55°
Color Temperature: 2,900k-3,050k   CRI: 100

AR70 Lamps

Halogen aluminum reflector lamps designed for display and accent lighting. The lamp and the faceted reflector together form a precision engineered light source. AR metal reflector lamps feature a central cap to prevent glare from the direct light beam.

15-50 Watts   2,000 Hours   Beam Angles: 6°-32°
Color Temperature: 3,000k   CRI: 100

PAR36 Lamps

Powerful halogen source producing an elliptical light pattern. The indirect nature of the lamp filament produces a uniquely powerful, low brightness source.

25-50 Watts   2,000-4,000 Hours   Beam Angles: 9°-51°
Color Temperature: 3,000k   CRI: 100

A/R/BR Lamps

"A" lamps are warm general service lamps, producing an omni-directional pattern of light. Inexpensive and readily available. BR lamps produce a warm even pattern of light along with an improved efficiency of 25% over obsolete R lamps.

30-300 Watts   2,000 Hours   Beam Angles: 22°-88°
Color Temperature: 2,700k   CRI: 100

Tungsten Halogen Lamps (T4)

Miniature halogen source provides excellent color rendering and light output.

55-150 Watts   2,500 Hours   Beam Angles: omni-directional
Color Temperature: 3,000k   CRI: 100

PAR16 Lamps

A line voltage version of the MR16 lamp, the PAR16 lamp provides many of the advantages of its low voltage counterpart in a select number of Beam Angles.

40-75 Watts   2,000 Hours   Beam Angles 10°-30°
Color Temperature: 3,000k   CRI: 100

PAR20/30/38 Lamps

Sophisticated optical packages with incandescent *or* tungsten halogen light sources and a wide array of Beam Angles. Energy saving lamps (enhanced for halogen) provide improved light output, greatly reducing energy consumption.

35-250 Watts   2,000-6,000 Hours   Beam Angles: 8°-60°
Color Temperature: 2,750k-3,000k   CRI: 100

Compact Fluorescent Lamps

Unique light source designed to integrate the efficiency of fluorescent lamps into the smaller lighting fixtures. Excellent for General lighting.

9-32 Watts   10,000 Hours   Beam Angles: omni-directional
Color Temperature: 2,700/3,000k/3,500k/4,100k   CRI: 82

HQI Lamps (T6)

The uniform color rendering of this source, in combination with its compact size, makes it ideal for lighting applications requiring high levels in a focused beam pattern. Fixture required to focus beam. See manufacturers' specs.

72 Watts   7,500 Hours   Beam Angles: omni-directional
Color Temperature: 3,000k   CRI: 85

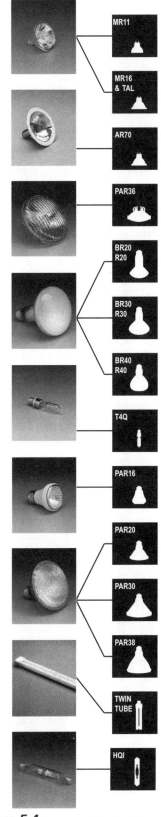

Figure 5.4   *Courtesy Capri*

Fixtures

There are many major manufacturers of recessed fixtures. Most offer complete catalogues with photometric information, lamp data, and installation requirements. This information is a must for the lighting designer. Manufacturers will send the information upon request. Several lighting manufacturers are listed in the *Resources* section of this manual.

While there will always be a place for decorative pendants, table lamps, torchieres, sconce lighting, as well as special function lighting, the lighting method of choice for residential is the recessed type. The goal is to have the source of light disappear leaving only the aesthetic effect the lighting gives the space.

Recessed Housings

Housings are recessed fixtures which can "house" a variety of line and low voltage lamp styles and wattages. These housings, or "cans," allow for connection to the electrical system, provide fire protection, and in conjunction with the variety of trims available, enhance or modify the inherent lighting characteristics of the lamp. Some are made for new construction and others are remodel types. Insulation can come in contact with some while it must be held back from others due to heat escape and fire prevention requirements. Being familiar with each type will enable the designer to select the most appropriate for the job when considering construction methods and local codes.

Ceiling openings can range from 2 inch to 10 inch diameters. Large openings, 8 inch diameter and greater, will appear too large for residential use. Some cans will fit within a 2 x 6 ceiling joist depth, others can exceed 14 inches. Not all trims will fit in all cans, so be sure to check manufacturer specifications.

The line drawings in this chapter represent a "nominal" size for the fixture types and should not be used as an installation specification.

New Construction Housings

For a new home under construction or when the drywall or plaster has been removed in a remodel, the new construction can is the best choice. It comes with bar hangers that mount to the joists which then allows the can to be slid back and forth on the bars to achieve the correct mounting position.

Figure 5.5   New Construction   *Capri*

Remodel Housings

Remodel cans can be installed through a round hole cut in the drywall or plaster. Special mounting clips hold the can to the ceiling material; similar to a molly fitting.

This will reduce drywall installation and patching costs. Don't forget, you must still be able to run the electrical feed to the can.

This fixture can also reduce the selection of some trims and lamps. They are available in both line and low voltage. Some manufacturers are producing this fixture in a type IC rating.

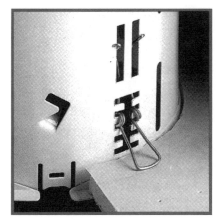

Figure 5.6   Remodel Can   *Capri*

Type IC (Insulation Contact Housings)

Type IC fixtures can be covered with insulation. Some states, like California, require that all cans be of the Type IC variety. The reason is that some residents have covered existing non-type IC cans with insulation being unaware that they were creating a fire hazard. Some jurisdictions do allow, however, "boxing" around a non-type IC fixture.

It is important to note that some fixtures, as yet, are not available in type IC so "boxing" or using an ICBO rated enclosure might be the only alternative. Type IC cans are often larger than their non-type IC counterparts which will need to be allowed for.

Figure 5.7   Type IC   *Capri*

Non-Type IC Housings

This fixture class has been around forever and is the most common and the least expensive. Typically, insulation must be held back 3" in all directions. Always check manufacturers' specifications and local codes.

Figure 5.8   Non-Type IC   *Capri*

Where insulation is not an issue, between floors and in soffits which are baffled from the main attic, this can may meet with building department approval.

Lets's move on and discuss some specific variations of these cans, the trims available, and how they affect the lighting output.

Trims for Recessed Cans

Housing trims finish off the hole in the ceiling, play an integral part in the photometry of a luminaire, and are available in several finishes.

Before looking at luminaires, it is best to understand some of the most common trims on the market and how they affect the quantity and color of the lighting we have so diligently been working to provide.

Black Milligroove Baffle

The most used trim in the field is the black step or milligroove baffle. It was one of the first trims made available and has, through shear volume, become the least expensive.

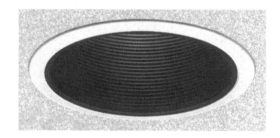

Figure 5.9   *Capri*

The original idea for the black color was that it reduced glare produced from the lamp. The problem is that it reduces glare mostly by absorbing 50% of the light. If a lamp produces 40 footcandles at a 5 foot distance, the black step baffle trim will reduce the footcandle level to 20! It is like throwing away half of your lighting energy dollar. From an aesthetic standpoint, the contrasting black trim in a white ceiling attracts attention from the focal point of any room. DON'T USE IT!

White Milligroove Baffle

Recently, manufacturers introduced a white version of the milligroove baffle. Using it will yield 70% of the available light. Much better than the black baffle and it blends with white ceilings.

Figure 5.10   *Capri*

Clear Specular/Alzak

The clear specular Alzak's mirrored surface allows virtually 100% of the light to exit the fixture and tends to reflect the color of the ceiling making it quite unobtrusive. Although more expensive than the black baffle, using Alzak trims will cut the fixture count in half, offsetting its higher price tag. The Alzak trim is by far the best choice and eliminates the "freckle" ceiling effect.

Figure 5.11   *Capri*

Note that a black Alzak will cut the light output by 50%, gold and rose colored Alzaks lose 10% **and** will change the color temperature of the light output.

Refer to *Appendix B*.

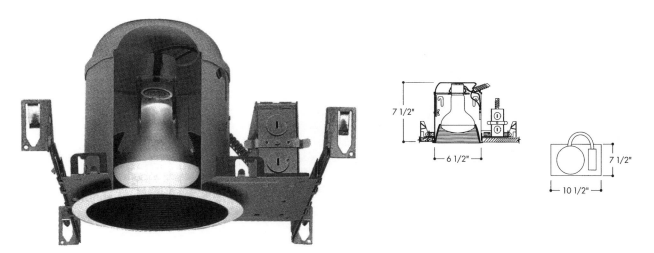

Figure 5.12   Recessed Non-Type IC Housing - R Lamp - Black Milligroove Trim   *Halo*

Recessed Luminaires

Remember that the housing, trim, and lamp combine to make what is known as a luminaire. It is the combination of the three that have a sum total effect on the quantity and quality of the light output.

Manufacturers publish lots of needed information on their housings including size, lamp, and wattage specifications. This information is a must. In this next section we will discuss issues that don't always find their way into the literature. We will look at the good and bad points of each luminaire along with, when applicable, ways to upgrade existing fixtures to provide better light output and efficiency.

Remodel housings are available for some of the fixtures. Check with your supplier.

Incandescent / Halogen Cans

Historically, the most often used combination for general lighting is that shown in Figure 5.12. It shows an R40 flood lamp and a black milligroove trim in a typical 7 inch recessed can. Unfortunately, this is the worst luminaire to use.

The R lamp is energy inefficient and now extinct through EPACT, the trim cuts 50% of the light output and is visually distracting. It has been a mainstay, however, simply because people have gotten used to it and, sometimes, that makes it desirable. Like a blind corner cabinet, this combination fills a need, but is such a waste.

A good retrofit is to replace the lamp with a more energy efficient PAR halogen lamp and an Alzak trim. The Alzak trim alone will double the light output without a change in lamp. Using a white milligroove baffle will yield 70% of the lamp output. When replacing an R40 flood with a PAR lamp, make sure to use a similar beam angle (over 50°). A compact fluorescent lamp designed to screw into the existing housing may protrude below the ceiling line and is considered, in a word, ugly. The compact fluorescent, in this case, will not produce enough light for kitchen or bath general lighting and the coverage will not be wide enough.

Figure 5.13   Recessed Type IC Housing - PAR Lamp - Black Milligroove Trim   *Halo*

This general lighting luminaire uses a PAR halogen lamp and a type IC housing which may come in contact with insulation. It still uses a black milligroove trim.

Like the previous luminaire, the Alzak or white milligroove trim will increase the light output and be less obtrusive.

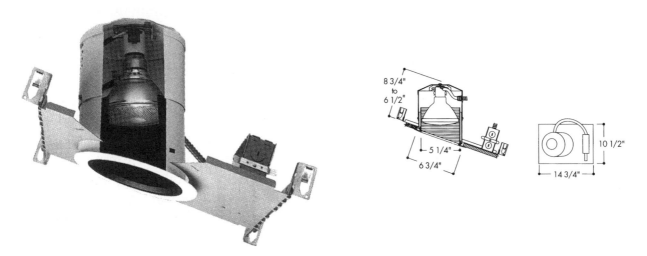

Figure 5.14   Sloped Ceiling Non-Type IC Housing - PAR Lamp - Black Milligroove Trim   *Halo*

This general lighting luminaire uses a PAR halogen lamp and a black milligroove trim in a non-type IC housing where insulation must be cut back. It needs an Alzak or white milligroove trim.

This fixture is used in vaulted ceilings so that the lamp can be oriented perpendicular to the floor. A housing designed for a flat ceiling installed in a vaulted one could direct the harsh glare of the lamp into the eyes of someone seated below.

Figure 5.15   ***Recessed Non-Type IC Housing - Vertical Double Twin Compact Fluorescent - White Milligroove Trim***

Halo

Compact Fluorescent Housings

The luminaire shown in Figure 5.15 uses a vertically oriented compact fluorescent and a white milligroove trim in a non-type IC housing. An Alzak will provide more light from the same lamp.

This is a good general lighting luminaire. Only one lamp in the fixture does not produce enough light to meet the foot-candle level requirements for a kitchen or bath. However, for a living, family or bedroom, it does an excellent job.

Notice that in a housing designed for a compact fluorescent, the lamp recesses far enough to be virtually unnoticed. Some manufacturers are producing a holder that resembles an R lamp which the compact fluorescent lamp slips into. Then the whole affair plugs into the housing. Again, for lower light level requirements, this solves the energy efficiency issues, as well as the aesthetic problems with the added bonus of no heat being introduced into the space from the lamps.

Designers will also be pleased with the high color rendering capabilities of this solution.

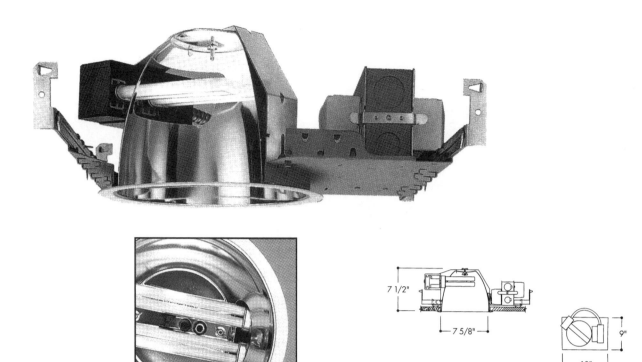

Figure 5.16   *Recessed Non-Type IC Housing - Horizontal Double Twin Compact Fluorescent -*
Alzak Trim

Halo/Prescolite

For kitchens or baths where the ceiling is being removed or in new construction, this is the luminaire to go with! It is powerful enough, it has the Alzak trim for maximum light output and the positioning of the lamps makes it the best looking, most efficient general lighting fixture on the market.

Through the use of two double twin compact fluorescent lamps, the luminaire easily achieves the footcandle level necessary in the kitchen or bath at a spacing that falls within the recommended 4 feet to 6 feet. The lamps are located at the top of the housing so one literally must be laying on the floor to see them. All that is seen is the reflected color of the ceiling in the trim.

When you think of it, any fluorescent lamp works best when the length of the tube presents itself to the space below. By mounting the lamps horizontally in this fixture, the trim needs to do less work in redirecting the light down into the space.

Some fixtures are outfitted with two ballasts, one for each lamp. It is possible to provide a cost effective quasi-dimming effect by running two switch legs to each fixture. One switch will operate ballast "A" and the other, ballast "B." In this manner, a hi-low beam effect is created much the same as headlights in a car. The room will have 50% or 100% light levels. This is a super solution if you have ever priced out dimmable ballasts.

Chapter 5 — Lamps & Fixtures

Figure 5.17   ***Recessed Non-Type IC Low Voltage Housing - MR 16 Lamp - Alzak Trim***   Halo

Low Voltage Housings

For accent and task lighting situations, it is hard to beat this 4" diameter luminaire. Figure 5.17 shows a usual housing with an aimable MR16 lamp and an Alzak trim. Since the transformer is built-in, the wiring is the same as that for line voltage housings. Some housings allow the lamp to be aimed up to 45° from vertical.

This gives a little latitude as to placement with respect to the object being illuminated and the general lighting grid. More on that in Chapter 6.

Note that, due to cost, low voltage lighting is normally not used for general illumination. There are always exceptions, however.

Most of the variables in low voltage lighting are built into the lamp itself or the trim being used in a standard housing so let's move on to trims.

Low Voltage Trims

Alzak, white and black milligroove trims are all available for low voltage housings as well. The discussions about these trims earlier in the chapter apply here too.

Figure 5.18   ***Alzak***   Capri

Figure 5.19   ***White Milligroove***   Capri

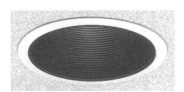

Figure 5.20   ***Black Milligroove***   Capri

Figure 5.21   **Pinhole Spot**   *Capri/Prescolite*

Pinhole Spot

When you want the lighting to disappear, the pinhole spot is the best. It is 4 inches in diameter with a 1 inch opening. Use this trim over sinks at windows or for island lighting. Not all housings allow for lamp angle adjustment; check specifications.

Unlike PAR or R lamps, MR lamps focus their beam several inches below the lamp (the ceiling with this trim). In other words, the beam does not become a wide angle until it is below the trim. *Cool!*

Eyelid

Use near the wall, usually within 12 inches, for wall washing and galleria wall lighting. This type of trim will cause much more light to fall on the top of a painting, for example, than the lower portion.

It is also useful for "grazing" a wall, accenting an unusual surface texture.

Also available in line voltage housings.

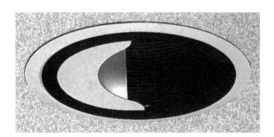

Figure 5.22   **Eyelid Wall Wash**   *Capri/Prescolite*

Adjustable

This trim allows the lamp to adjust within the housing so nothing protrudes below the ceiling line. It may clip the beam in wider angle lamps.

Also available in line voltage housings. Aiming angle is measured from vertical.

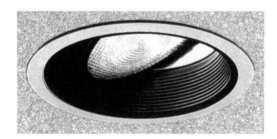

Figure 5.23   **Adjustable**   *Capri/Prescolite*

Figure 5.24   Eyeball   *Capri/Prescolite*

Eyeball 45° x 360°

The eyeball trim is a versatile lamp for art lighting. It can be swiveled left to right 360° and aimed up to 45° from vertical. Make sure the center of your artwork is within the trims adjustment range!

This trim, however, protrudes below the ceiling line and normally has a black trim; both attract the eye.

Also available in line voltage housings.

See Chapter 7, Art Lighting for more on positioning the lamps for art.

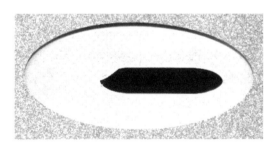

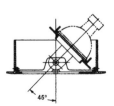

Figure 5.25   Oval Slot   *Capri/Prescolite*

Oval Slot 45° x 360°

The perfect art lighting trim. It has the same range of adjustment as the eyeball without any of the factors which can draw the eye. Accent lighting on wall hung art or a floor sculpture can be achieved without any part of the luminaire projecting from the ceiling and the small aperture is very inconspicuous. Be careful that the aiming angle range of the housing is adequate to hit the center of the art.

Aiming angle is measured from vertical.

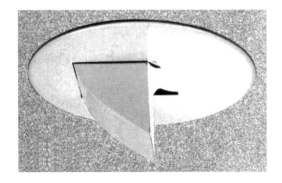

Figure 5.26   **Mirror Light**   *Capri/Prescolite*

Figure 5.27   **Framing Projector**   *Prescolite*

Mirror Light 90° x 360°

Another great art lighting trim when there are less than perfect factors in the room. This trim can swivel 360° and can adjust from vertical to 90°. When a joist or other obstruction prevents positioning the housing within the normal vertical to 45° range or when there is a vaulted ceiling, this trim is adjustable enough to hit the art.

The projecting portion is outfitted with a mirror and reflects the light from the lamp to the object being illuminated. This trim will provide light straight down to the floor all the way up to where the ceiling meets the wall! The art has to be in there somewhere.

Aiming angle is measured from vertical.

Framing Projector 90° x 360°

This framing projector looks just like the mirror light trim but, has a built-in technology which allows the beam to be focused to fit the art. Some framing projectors house a matt which is cut to the shape of the art. Whether rectangular, square, or diamond shaped, the beam conforms to fit without spill light. A dramatic effect.

Aiming angle is measured from vertical.

While not exhaustive, the preceding trims are the most common to residential lighting. Most trims are available for 4 inch and 7 inch diameter housings. Not all trims are available on all housings due to lamp size, heat restrictions, housing size (shallow cans), etc. Check manufacturers specifications.

Low Voltage Special Effects Filters

Fixtures which house MR16 lamps provide a safety lens placed in front of the lamp to prevent any portion of the lamp from "popping" off and causing injury when the lamp burns out. This safety filter does not change the characteristics of the lamp. Many filters are available which can be substituted for the safety filter which can greatly affect the normal beam pattern and color.

The three most popular of these filters are the spread lens which widens the beam angle about 15%, the beam elongator which lengthens the beam in one direction only, and the soft focus lens which softens the light and reduces the prismatic "sparkles" which can sometimes occur.

Figures 5.29 - 5.32 illustrate the effects of the spread, beam elongator, and soft focus lenses when used on a MR16 ESX narrow spot.

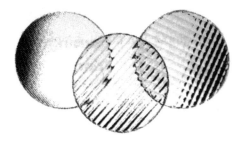

Figure 5.28   ***Soft Focus, Spread, and Beam Elongator***   *Halo*

Figure 5.29   ***ESX w/ Clear Lens***

Figure 5.31   ***ESX w/ Beam Elongator***

Figure 5.30   ***ESX w/ Spread Lens***

Figure 5.32   ***ESX w/ Soft Focus***   *Ardee*

When using a spread lens, understand that you are increasing the beam angle which will reduce the candlepower by approximately the same 15%. The beam elongator can be rotated from a horizontal orientation to vertical.

There are also a variety of colored filters. Halo makes one that can change the color temperature of a MR16 lamp from 3,000k to 2,700k.

Various Colored Filters   *Halo*

The best thing to do is to experiment with the many filters to create the effects you would like or that the project requires. I have learned so many things by trial and error. I hope this saves you a little time.

Surface Wall (Sconce)

These fixtures mount on the wall and either shed their light upward, downward, forward, or any combination of the three. They are wonderful for creating a mood and for filling facial shadows in a bathroom. Choose these fixtures for the effect you want.

Be careful about placement. It is possible to see into the top of some fixtures exposing the wiring and lamp to view.

No photometrics are available for sconce type lighting.

Surface Ceiling (Pendant)

A virtually infinite number of styles, colors, and lamp types are available from manufacturers the world over. Have fun.

For 8 foot ceilings, when placing a pendant over an eating surface, allow 25 inches to 30 inches above the table or counter. For each additional foot of ceiling height raise the pendant 3 inches.

A pendant over a table should approach 20 inches in diameter and should be 12 inches less in width than that of the table.

When planning for a ceiling fan, most building codes require a special metal box to be securely fastened to the joists.

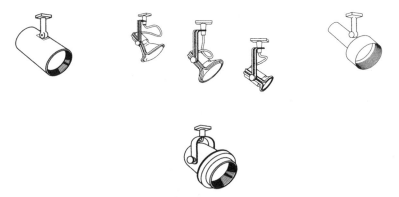

Figure 5.33   ***Track Mounted Mono-Points***   *Prescolite*

Track Lighting

Track lighting is a system that utilizes a surface mounted track which can receive mono-point fixtures anywhere along its length. Track is the most versatile of the luminaire systems in that the luminaire can be repositioned down the road as needed for furniture placement change. The advantages are that you can decide the position of the lamp holders after installation using an incredible diversity of styles. The disadvantages are that they attract the attention of the viewer, diluting the focal point of any room. Sometimes, however, they are the only choice when structural restrictions, such as limited attic space or unfortunately placed ducting or plumbing prohibit the use of the more unobtrusive recessed fixtures. It is in this case that I thank God for the existence of track lighting.

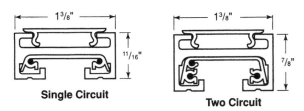

Figure 5.34   ***Track Types***   *Prescolite*

The two main types of tracks are *single* and *two* circuit as shown in Figure 5.34. The single circuit can receive one switch leg while the two circuit can have two switch legs which control two sets of mono-points independently regardless of position or order along the track. When possible, mount the track flush with the ceiling material to make it less noticeable.

There are many variations on fittings and connectors available; too many to go into here. However, in figure 5.35, the most common are listed. Read through the list and take particular note of the two **Mono-Point** adapters which can be mounted in a 3 inch round rough in box and eliminates the need for the track. The mono-point snaps into the adapter instead of the track. To use this nifty little adapter, you will need to determine the positioning ahead of time using the same spacing procedures you are already familiar with from Chapter 3, *Spacing Principles*.

End Feed - feed from above for direct conduit or pendant feed.

Outlet Box Feed - feed connector with built-in outlet box cover and mounting strap.

"L"/Straight Feed Connector - joins two track sections to make 90° angle or straight run. Right angle and straight covers included.

"T" Feed Connector - joins three track sections at 90° angles.

"X" Feed Connector - joins four track sections at 90° angles.

Flexible Connector - connects two track sections for vertical or horizontal bends up to 90°.

T-Bar Feed - for feeding track mounting directly on T-Bar 1/2" K.O.

Outlet Box Cover Plate - for use with **TS-14/15/16** when feeding at outlet box.

Floating Feed - permits mounting track to outer box located anywhere along the track. Includes extra track dead end.

Mini Connector - joins two track sections together. Note: Not a feed connector.

Wire Mold Feed - use with wire mold raceway #200. Equipped with mechanical wire mold ground.

Surface Conduit Feed - for surface wiring. Standard 1/2" connector.

Mono Point - allows line voltage fixture to be converted to canopy mount installation.
(4^{7}/$_{8}$" dia. x ^{7}/$_{8}$")

Electronic Low Voltage Mono Point - allows miniature, electronic low voltage fixtures to be converted to canopy mount installation.

Weighted Base - for use with all fixture models supplied with 6' cord, plug and integral switch.

Stem Kit* - canopy mount. Attaches to outlet box or ceiling 4 1/2" dia. canopy. 18" long stem. Space no further than 4' apart. Contact factory for other pendant lengths. Attaches to track, not feed connectors.

Extension Wands - mounts to track and extends fixture.

18" line volt. wand	18" low volt. wand
24" line volt. wand	24" low volt. wand
36" line volt. wand	

Figure 5.35   *Track Fittings and Connectors*   *Prescolite*

Low Voltage Track Filters

Many accessories are available to change the "off the shelf" characteristics of the lamp and/or luminaire to suit a variety of design needs. Experiment with them to see how they actually work in the field.

In Figure 5.36, a variety of filters and toys are shown. Some are similar to those already discussed along with some additional devices. Some mount directly onto the mono-point fixture rather than the lamp.

Another little device is the barn door.

Barn doors limit the amount of spill light, reducing glare, and can frame an object more tightly.

We will look at good and bad examples of track use in Chapter 6, *Practical Application.*

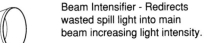
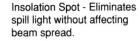

Beam Elongator - Projects light in a elongated pattern allowing for full illumination.

Beam Intensifier - Redirects wasted spill light into main beam increasing light intensity.

Insolation Spot - Eliminates spill light without affecting beam spread.

Color Filter Retainer - For use with optional color filters.

45° cutoff baffle - Increases lamp cutoff angle from standard 30° to full 45° cutoff.

Spread Lens - Smooths and spreads the main beam creating a wider and more uniform pattern.

Hexcell Louver - Black egg crate type louver provides 45° cutoff to lamp.

Softening Lens - Smooths out the main beam eliminating the striations, hot spots and un-evenness of the bare lamp.

Figure 5.36   ***Low Voltage Track Filters***   *Prescolite*

Counter Lighting

There are many lighting fixtures on the market designed to be placed under the wall cabinets whose sole purpose is to provide task lighting to the counter. All under-cabinet lighting should be placed near the front of the cabinet behind the light rail.

Bear in mind that the lights illuminate both the counter and the backsplash. The closer the lights are placed together and the more evenly they are spaced along the wall cabinets, the more even the illumination will be to both the backsplash and the counter.

Puck Lighting

Some fixtures, such as puck lights are spaced up to 18 inches apart. This leads to light and dark areas across the backsplash. Often the backsplash is designed to be a decorative element. The "pools" of light will detract from the beauty.

When mounting the puck in the top of a glass door display cabinet with glass shelves, remember that the light diminishes to each successive shelf below the lamp, not to mention the cumulative shadows of objects placed on the shelves.

Hiding the wiring is another problem with the puck system.

Under-Cabinet Fluorescent

Under-cabinet fluorescents do not render good color, the T5 lamps being only available in cool and warm white. The fixture lengths available are limited which necessitates gaps between fixtures. This, again produces the light/dark effect across the backsplash.

Chapter 5 — Lamps & Fixtures

Low Voltage Strip Lighting

Low voltage fixtures which use festoon or halogen lamps are single strips with lamps as little as 2 inches apart. Metal strips which hold the lamps are available in any length, in 2 inch increments, up to 12 feet! This produces a very even illumination to the counter and to the backsplash. When using festoons, use frosted ones to reduce glare and diffuse the light.

Figure 5.38   **Clear & Frosted Festoons**

Ardee

By going to a 4 inch spacing on the lamps, this fixture works well for toe kick, over-cabinet lighting, and mounted vertically behind the stiles of a glass door display cabinet.

Go over the wiring specifications carefully. The wire necessary is often 10 - 12 gauge. The closer the transformer is placed to the lamps, the smaller the wire gauge can be. I will often place the transformer in a base lazy susan under the counter. This keeps it accessible, dampens transformer noise, and is close to the lamps. Transformers should be rated 20% greater than the overall wattage of the lamps.

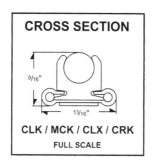

CROSS SECTION

9/16"

13/16"

CLK / MCK / CLX / CRK

FULL SCALE

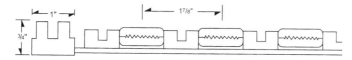

1"   17/8"

3/4"

Figure 5.37   **Festoon Strip**   *Ardee*

If the light strip has pre-installed lamps, the installation cost is reduced when compared to modular units that come in 4 inch units which need to be assembled like an erector set. Figure 5.37 shows an excellent example of a lighting strip for under-cabinet use.

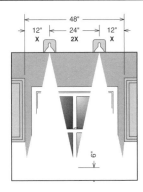

CHAPTER 6

PRACTICAL APPLICATION

You have worked hard on the fundamental concepts of lighting, how color affects lighting and how lighting affects color. You have learned how to establish a footcandle level for the various rooms in the house and how to adjust those levels for a variety of conditions; reflectance, age, and specific activities to be performed in these rooms. You can space the lighting appropriately for both general and task lighting situations by using either a protractor or the spacing table. You can determine the proper lamp using either the Inverse Square Law or the Lumen Method. In other words... you are better versed in lighting than most of the people who actually specify lighting for residential projects. Give yourself a well earned pat on the back.

It is now time to rest your weary mind and simply recap all that we have learned and organize it into a matter of steps and in what order they should occur. We will work through some kitchen and bath lighting plans and discuss some special situations. Then, through, a series of photographs, we will discuss real life design problems and solutions with advice on how to overcome often encountered dilemmas.

We won't go over the calculations again to avoid becoming redundant, rather, we will concentrate on layout, structural, architectural, and aesthetic issues.

The topics in this Chapter are:

- **Seven Steps of Lighting**

- **Kitchen Lighting Plans**

  - Lighting at a Window

- **Kitchen Lighting**

  - The Good and the Bad

- **Bath Lighting Plan**

  - Lighting the Face

- **Bath Lighting**

- **Miscellaneous Issues**

  - Switching

  - Structural Considerations

Seven Steps of Lighting

It might be handy to see, all together, a listing of what order things should be done when setting about to effect a lighting plan.

1 If at all possible, determine the colors in the room. Remember light is an additive and every time it bounces off a surface it adds to the overall lighting in the room. Reflectance is one of the factors involved when adjusting the base footcandle level in the room. If the colors are not known, consider them to be "medium" reflectance. This is covered in Chapter 2, *Reflectance*.

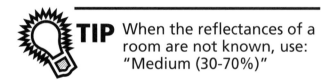 **TIP** When the reflectances of a room are not known, use: "Medium (30-70%)"

2 Determine the footcandle level for the room you are working with and adjust for reflectance and occupant age. The footcandle level is what you are actually "shooting" for when performing the upcoming lighting calculations. Don't forget to do task lighting levels where it is appropriate. This is covered in Chapter 4, *Lighting Calculations*.

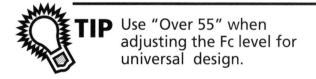 **TIP** Use "Over 55" when adjusting the Fc level for universal design.

 **TIP** If reflectances are not known, use:

	General	Task
Kitchen	40 Fc	100 Fc
Bath	40 Fc	

General Lighting

3 Have an idea of whether you are planning on using halogen or fluorescent lamping and the size of the fixtures which will house them. It is a real good idea to be familiar with the direction of the joists or trusses, as well as any restrictions concerning height and insulation codes. This may restrict your selection of recessed cans, for example, to the IC type. The on-center spacing of the ceiling framing will also affect the spacing of the fixtures.

 **TIP** Maintain 48" - 72" spacing for general lighting.

Once you have an idea of the spacing that is possible, you can establish, using the Spacing Table in chapter 3, the beam angle that will work for you. A good starting point to work toward is 48" - 72" for general lighting. If you are using fluorescent, Step 8 on the lumen method calculation work sheet will give the spacing of the luminaire.

4 If you are planning directional lamps, the Inverse Square Law can be used to find the candlepower of the lamp which will produce the footcandle level you have already decided is necessary.

If you are using fluorescent, or have a CU rating on the luminaire, you can use the Lumen Method to determine the number of luminaires needed for the room and the spacing required to maintain the footcandle level.

Both of these methods are explained in Chapter 4, *Lighting Calculations.*

5 After using one of the two calculation methods, you can begin your search of *Appendix A* in either the incandescent or fluorescent section for a lamp that will do the job.

TIP Color Temperatures:

Cool 3,600k-5,500k
Neutral 3,000k-3,600k
Warm 2,700k-3,000k

It is important, at this point, to consider the color temperature and the CRI of the lamp. I recommend finding lamps in the 2,900k to 3,600k range **and** over 80 CRI.

TIP Use lamps between 2,900k - 3,600k for most general & task lighting.

In a room, lamps should appear to be the same color temperature.

Halogen lamps run about 3,000k and 100 CRI. These are great with regard to color and efficiency. Fluorescent lamping runs the gamut of color temperature and CRI. I recommend either 3,000k or 3,500k and over 80 CRI. If you want to match your halogen task and accent lamps, use a fluorescent at 3,500k. Horizontally mounted compact fluorescent lamps in recessed cans are a nice choice for kitchen or bath general lighting.

Dimming a lamp will cause it to look warmer.

Make sure to familiarize yourself with the CU tables in *Appendix B* for luminaire comparisons.

6 Lay out a ceiling grid that fits within your spacing parameters and as set forth in the Spacing Table in Chapter 3 or according to the results of step 8 of the Lumen Method work sheet. This, of course, is for general lighting. Task lighting is next.

TIP Cones of light should intersect above the work plane for best coverage.

TIP Spacing between lamps should be twice that at the ends.

TIP Always think of spacing in terms of evenly distributed half cones.

Task Lighting

7 All wall cabinetry over countertops should receive under-cabinet lighting to raise the task lighting footcandle level to the appropriate level, eliminate shadows, and evenly illuminate the backsplash. Remember to place the lighting at the front of the wall cabinet behind the light rail for good coverage and diffusion. Discussions concerning counter lighting are found in Chapters 1, 3, and 5.

Additional lighting will be required where there are no wall cabinets above, such as at a window, island, and peninsula. I like to vary the physical size or shape of these fixtures so they don't become confused with the visual symmetry of the general lighting fixtures. This can be achieved by using pendants or the smaller 4 inch diameter recessed cans which are discussed in Chapter 5.

In bathrooms, the task lighting comes in the form of wall mounted fixtures or sconces which illuminate the face for applying make up or shaving. If at all possible, try to distribute these face illuminating fixtures (approximately at eye level) evenly throughout all mirrored areas. If not, at least place them at the vanity. These fixtures should be placed between 2 feet to 3 feet apart and evenly spaced from the center of the users face.

Task lamping for the shower and for reading in the tub is also recommended. Be sure to check local codes which restrict the type of fixture allowable and the height at which they are placed above wet areas. Damp location approved lamps are available from all the major manufacturers.

For closets, lensed fixtures are often required to meet local codes to prevent someone from inadvertently sticking a hanger up into the fixture.

Kitchen Lighting Plan 1

Let's go through the process of laying out a lighting plan for the kitchen depicted in figure 6.1 through 6.4.

This is a small kitchen set in a high rise with slab to slab construction. The ceiling had to be dropped to accommodate ductwork for heating. At one end of the room are floor to ceiling windows with a 3 inch vertical center mullion.

The kitchen design left a somewhat challenging "J" shaped work aisle. The general lighting had to be symmetrical with the vertical window mullion.

To find a workable general lighting arrangement, I will often try ceiling grid patterns printed out on clear mylar with various spacings. Lay the mylar on the floor plan and slide it around so you can see the relationships. I settled on a 4 x 4 foot grid of 16 cans with a 30 inch spacing centered on the window. This pattern also lined up nicely with the work aisle.

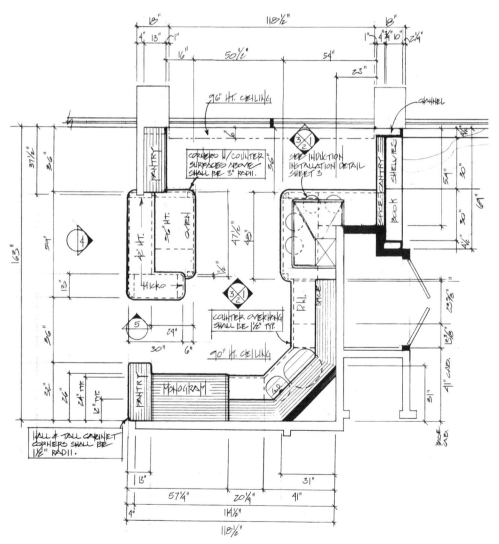

Figure 6.1   Kitchen 1 Floor Plan

Six cans were removed from the sink and cooktop areas since the wall jogged in and under-cabinet and hood lighting would illuminate the counters. Two additional cans were removed over the under-counter oven counter since they did not position well over that work space. This left eight cans following the "J" shaped floor space.

Three smaller cans, which provided a higher footcandle level, were then positioned over the oven work counter. The change in size allowed them to coexist visually with the general lighting grid.

Here is a little trick. By placing the lamps so that the spacing is exactly half of the

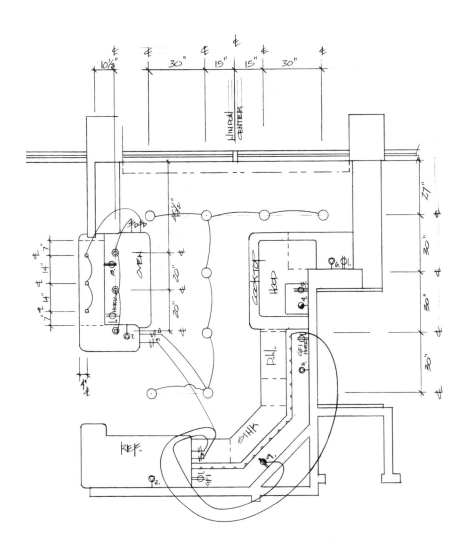

Figure 6.2   Kitchen 1 Lighting Plan   *MDL & A*

Michael De Luca CKD, ASID   *Photo Glen Cormier*

Figure 6.3   Kitchen 1

width of the cone at the work plane, the footcandle level will increase by about 50% and you will still have an even field of light. So, if the width of the cone (maximum spacing) is 60 inches, reduce your spacing to half of that (30 inches). The edge of one cone will be at the center of the next cone. With the dark materials used in this kitchen, it was necessary to do this as the more tightly spaced grid worked better with the kitchen design and the architecture of the room.

The decorative pendant over the table gives a nice variation to the ceiling elements and complements the decor.

Michael De Luca CKD, ASID   *Photo Glen Cormier*

Figure 6.4   Kitchen 1

Kitchen Lighting Plan 2

Our second kitchen plan is larger and more complex. Here we have a center island with a skylight over it, a sitting area serving as a mini family room, and an informal dining area.

The problem is to provide general and task illumination for the kitchen, in addition to general lighting for the sitting and dining areas.

Again, start with a grid. In this case,

there was no way for one grid to work for the entire room. Starting in the "L" shape kitchen corner, the grid was laid out symmetrically in the corner 48 inches out from either wall with a 51 inch spacing between lamps. Two of the fixtures fell in the skylight so they were eliminated. The resulting four fixtures became the general lighting for the main working area of the kitchen. Alzak trims on 7 inch fixtures were used with PAR38 halogen lamps.

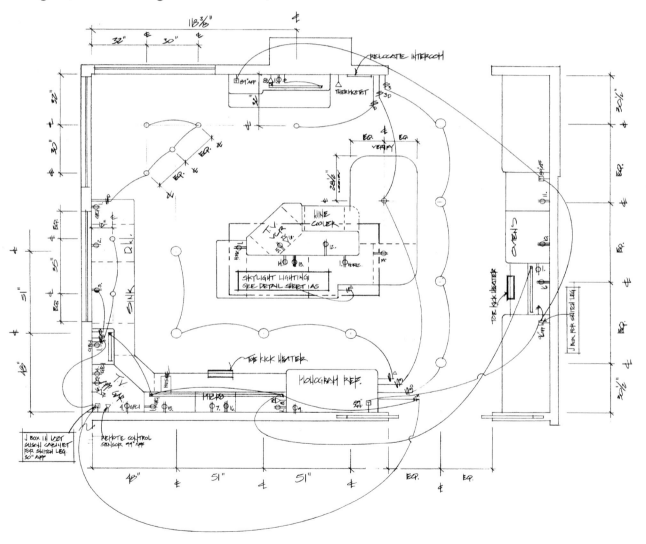

Figure 6.5   Kitchen Lighting Plan 2

MDL & A

Michael De Luca CKD, ASID   *Photo McKay Photographics*

Figure 6.6   Kitchen 2

Across the oven wall, a row of fixtures were spaced 51 inches apart and 51 inches away from the first grid and on the center line of the doorways. The spacing interval of 51 inches did not happen by accident. It was calculated from the center of the doorways across the refrigerator wall to the first lamp above the corner lazy susan. When possible, try to get all the intervals to be equal. Having done this, the general lighting layout is complete for the work aisles.

Try to find a beam angle that allows your grid to fall at least 15 inches in front of 24 inch depth tall cabinets to minimize scallops. This will be at least 39 inches out from the wall.

The general lighting for the sitting area was then laid out so that the lamps followed the front of the banquette. Doing this keeps the lamps out in front of the person seated and prevents ghoulish shadows on the face. A fourth lamp was placed over the coffee table completing a triangle of light. MR16 lamps in 4 inch diameter recessed cans with alzak trims were used here to match the style of the main lighting, but due to the smaller size are not visually a part of the main lighting.

Task lighting is next with typical under-cabinet lighting for the counters. Notice the J-box locations for low voltage transformers.

Michael De Luca CKD, ASID   *Photo McKay Photographics*

Figure 6.7   Kitchen 2

We wired these future transformer locations for above cabinet lighting should they ever decide to add it. Wiring is cheap.

Two chrome rods which house recessed track are installed up inside the skylight, out of view, and perpendicular to the refrigerator wall. Using four mono-point fixtures in these tracks provide task lighting to the working portion of the island. I like the subtle irony of the light coming out of the skylight at night.

Two recessed cans outfitted with pinhole spot trims are placed along the window over the main kitchen sink which hide nicely and don't visually conflict with either the 4 inch or 7 inch open Alzaks.

A pendant is placed over the built-in island table. The use of a well placed pendant or pendants provides a balancing downward movement to the upward movement caused by the skylight.

A single recessed MR16 provides light to the open cookbook shelves at the desk with under-cabinet lighting for the work surface.

Notice the practical placement of switches and which groups of fixtures they control. By grouping the lighting circuits in this way, and the use of dimmers, a variety of functional and mood lighting scenarios can be achieved.

Task Lighting at a Window

Designing task lighting at a window can be easily done if you keep in mind the cones of light and the spacing issues discussed in Chapter 3.

A common task lighting situation at a window is shown in figure 6.8. The window is 36 inches wide with 6 inches on either side for casing and wall surface. Flanking the area are wall cabinets. The counter area to be lit is 24 inches by 48 inches.

You can see that by using two lamps (4 half cones) the 48 inch wide space can be divided into 12 inch sections. One section at each wall cabinet and two sections (24 inches) between lamps. Using the spacing table, it is a simple matter to find a beam angle for the lamp. Let's assume a 5 foot distance.

Using the spacing table, Chapter 3, look across the 4.5 foot distance row (remember we want a 6 inch intersect above the counter) until you find the 24 inch spacing wanted. Now travel up the column to find the beam angle (25°). By looking in the 5 foot row, you will find this cone of light is 27 inches wide at the counter. Perfect. Place the lamp 12 inches out from the wall to center the cone on the counter depth. You can use the candlepower table in Chapter 4 to find the candlepower for 100 footcandles of task lighting. In the 5 foot row, travel across to the 100 Fc column to find 2,500 Cp.

This is a much better solution than one lamp. If one lamp is to provide light across the 48 inch counter, it will also be 48 inches in depth which will cause an unsightly scallop on the window or window treatment.

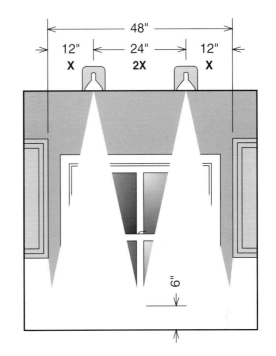

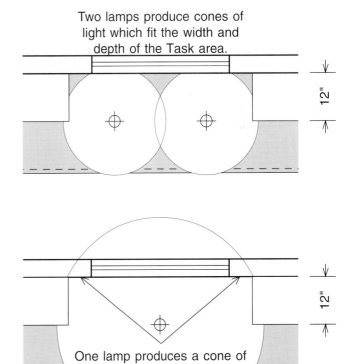

Two lamps produce cones of light which fit the width and depth of the Task area.

One lamp produces a cone of light which is too deep for the countertop causing a large scallop on the wall.

Figure 6.8   Task Lighting at a window

Kitchen Lighting
The Good and the Bad

Lighting Problems

One of the best ways for a designer to assimilate new information is through visual example. We can learn as much from good examples as the bad. I much prefer staying on the positive side, but there are some definite kitchen lighting killers that you must see to fully appreciate. After the main lighting problems are discussed we will look at examples of kitchens that are good solutions.

The kitchen shown in figure 6.9 meets all the lighting requirements concerning spacing and footcandle levels. However, the use of the black step-baffle trims detract from the design of the room and cut out 50% of the light the lamp produces. This is the epitome of inefficiency. Notice how the sharp contrast between the black trim and the white ceiling draws your eye.

The pinhole spot trims are correctly located at the center of each arched window. This is an important detail which should never be overlooked. See, even in the bad there is always good.

Another thing I learned from this kitchen is that a variety of lighting fixture types adds to the interest of the room; no less than introducing an angle or depth change in cabinetry. Instead of the four small recessed cans over the island, a group of pendants would have been more interesting.

Avoid using lamps of mixed color temperature when illuminating objects that occur throughout an area such as a backsplash or counter.

Michael De Luca CKD, ASID   *Photo MDL & A*

Figure 6.9   *Swiss Cheese Ceiling*

Photo NKBA

Figure 6.10   *Mixed Color Temperatures*

Figure 6.10 shows a natural woodgrain backsplash with halogen puck lights in the soffit, cool white fluorescent in the hood, and warm incandescent under the cabinets.

Note how the color of the backsplash appears differently under each light source. Try to match the color temperature of lamps as much as possible in this situation. It is okay to mix incandescent, fluorescent, and halogen as long as they appear to be the same color. See Chapter 2 for more on color temperature and CRI.

Photo NKBA

Figure 6.11   Scallops on Wall Cabinets

Figure 6.11 shows how mounting the light source too close to the wall cabinetry will cause unsightly scallops. The face of all cabinetry should blend to give an even appearance. Chapter 3 deals with this and other spacing issues.

Photo NKBA

Figure 6.12   Uneven Backsplash Lighting

Avoid under-cabinet lighting which produces "pools" of light across the

backsplash. This creates visual "chop" and weakens the impact of any backsplash material.

The secret to even counter and back-splash lighting is in using strip lighting where the lamps are spaced 2 inches on center. Figure 6.12 uses fluorescent fixtures which come in limited widths which translates into gaps between fixtures. T5 lamps which are used in these fixtures are only available in low quality cool and warm white. Chapter 3 contains solutions for backsplash lighting and Chapter 5 gives examples of suitable fixtures.

Figure 6.13   Track

The last thing I want to dissuade you from using is surface mounted track in a kitchen as shown in figure 6.13.

If you consider the elements and principles of design, this solution visually does not work. The track breaks plane with the ceiling, the mono-points are all aimed on divergent dynamic angles, and each is outfitted with a black baffle; all these are elements which attract the viewers attention away from the design below.

This is a shame when there are better methods available to achieve the same lighting effect. Recessed fixtures break none of the aforementioned rules and therefore remain unobtrusive, especially when outfitted with an Alzak trim which tends to reflect the color of the ceiling.

Now that we have pointed out what to avoid, let's look at some solutions.

Kitchen Lighting Solutions

I have tried to group the following photos into specific areas; recessed lighting, counter lighting, track, and art lighting. However, there are overlapping issues in some of the photos which are worthy of mention. So I will.

Recessed Trim & Pendant

Figure 6.14 depicts an award winning contemporary design with excellent attention to good lighting practice.

The white trims blend with the ceiling and therefore do not detract from the variety of ceiling heights and shapes. White trims absorb about 30% of the available light from the lamp.

Barton A. Lidsky

Photo Peter Rymwid

Figure 6.14 **White Recessed Trim & Pendants**

The cooking center has light provided to it through the use of two recessed fixtures as well as the hood light.

The sleek pendants at the vegetable prep counter complement the angled shape and material used in the hood.

A circular soffit mirrors the round table while allowing dedicated lighting for informal dining.

Figure 6.15 shows the use of the alzak trim in the recessed ceiling fixtures. Alzak permits virtually **all** of the light to exit the fixture, tends to reflect the color of the ceiling and visually disappears.

The two alabaster pendants are an excellent choice, providing greater illumination to the island while setting off the neo-classic period style.

Notice the use of the sconce which frames this beautiful kitchen. Switched separately, these can provide light for getting a cup of coffee or wine while watching a movie in the adjoining room.

Take particular note of the evenly illuminated backsplash.

The lighting in this kitchen provides function and, I am sure, many referrals.

Eugene Nahemow/David Rivera

Photo Jay Graham

Figure 6.15   *Alzak Recessed Trim & Pendant*

Figure 6.16 shows a general lighting grid pattern which will provide a very even field of illumination.

A recessed section of track holds a series of mono-point pendants for task lighting at the island. This is an excellent use of track; one piece running center and parallel to the length of the island. Since four fixtures were used relatively close together, a more subtle, smaller, and color coordinated fixture selection seems most appropriate. The pizza looks good too!

Karen Edwards, CKD   *Photo Maura McEvoy*

Figure 6.16   ***Great General Lighting Grid and Use of Track***

Karen Edwards, CKD   *Photo Maura McEvoy*

Figure 6.17   ***A Most Creative Chandelier***

At the opposite end of the kitchen, figure 6.17, is located a dining table with a most interesting arrangement of pendants. Notice how the designer has taken three separate pendants, varied the length of the cords, and grouped them together to form an attractive chandelier. *Very cool!*

Both islands on this page use pendants for task level lighting. It is important to note that the period style of the room plays a big part in the selection of an appropriate pendant. Note the yellow cast of the incandescent lighting in figure 6.18 while the single halogen fixture in figure 6.19 throws a more neutral white. Remember color is still an individual choice and beauty is in the eye...

Susan Sprouse/Marilyn Miller/Terry Cunningham   *Photo Rip Noel*

Figure 6.18   *Three Gorgeous Pendants*

Michael De Luca, CKD, ASID   *Dupont Corian*

Figure 6.19   *Halogen Pendant at Island*

Counter/Backsplash Lighting

In kitchen lighting, there is nothing more important than the lighting at the functional surfaces of the room; the countertop. The backsplash often provides a dramatic backdrop to the kitchen that envelops it. It is imperative that the proper footcandle level be provided to the counter surfaces and that the backsplash maintain an even field of continuous illumination for aesthetic effect. See Chapter 4 for more.

The designer of the kitchen in figure 6.20 takes this one step beyond in his consideration of the motif of the room, as well as the view to the outside. Notice the use of pendants regularly placed between evenly spaced windows. This provides symmetry, rhythm, and even illumination.

During the day, the pendants complement the vintage look while they take center stage as the panarama falls into the ebon grasp of night.

Tom Trzcinski, CKD, CBD

Photo Wayne Simco

Figure 6.20   Pendant Task Lighting at Window Wall

Michael De Luca, CKD, ASID/Judith Carmichael, CKD, IIDA   *WesTech*

Figure 6.21   Even Splash Lighting

The backsplash in figure 6.21 is as it should appear. Note the even illumination from one end of the kitchen to the other. Counter lighting becomes even more important as the color of the material darkens.

The kitchen shown in figure 6.22 has a curved stainless steel hood flanked by two granite walls. An obvious focal point. With no wall cabinetry under which lighting can be mounted and the ceiling being consumed by the skylight, a creative solution was found in the use of recessed MR16 fixtures outfitted with mirror light trims introduced in Chapter 5.

Notice the small triad of mirror lights grouped in the ceiling to the right of the skylight. By nesting them together, the ceiling outside the skylight did not become visually congested and the mirror lights' great adjustability allowed aiming to the counter sections on either side of the cooktop and at the hood itself. The hood light takes care of the barbecue.

Michael De Luca, CKD, ASID   *MDL & A*

Figure 6.22   Grouped Mirror Light Trims

Skylights and Beamed Ceilings

Skylight openings are very strong architectural elements. Care should be taken to symmetrically place lighting about them. The kitchen in figure 6.23 uses nicely placed vaulted ceiling adapters to keep the lamps perpendicular to the floor while accommodating the pitch of the ceiling. These adapters are adjustable and are now available in white and Alzak trims.

Gary Johnson   *Photo David Livingston*

Figure 6.23   Vaulted Ceiling

Michael De Luca, CKD, ASID   *MDL & A*

Figure 6.24   Pinhole Spots at Skylight

The recessed fixtures are arranged at the corners of the skylight in figure 6.24. The recessed task fixtures use the oval slot to direct the light where needed on the island while allowing a pleasing arrangement relative to the skylight and to the general lighting fixtures. Changing the task lighting to the smaller 4 inch diameter MR16 can eliminate confusion of the ceiling and allows more flexibility in their placement.

Note the two pinhole spots centered on the window.

Open beams are another architectural element which affects the placement of lighting fixtures whether they be surface mounted or recessed.

The kitchen in figure 6.25 shows the recessed general lighting centered between beams.

The ledge which has been created around the perimeter of the room serves two important purposes. First, it allows for counter lighting at the windows and second, it accommodates fluorescent fixtures which bounce indirect light off the ceiling. Any gaps between the indirect lighting fixtures will result in dark areas on the ceiling.

Low voltage festoon strip lighting is used under-cabinet.

A last note here, the french door at the pantry will receive a shear curtain which hides the contents, yet provides a nice accent light

Michael De Luca, CKD, ASID

MDL & A

Figure 6.25   *Beamed Ceiling and Indirect Lighting Ledge*

Figure 6.26   Fluorescent Ceiling Conversion

The aluminum ceiling system was removed, a ledger was added around the perimeter of the existing ceiling well, the fluorescent fixtures were tossed out, and the surfaces were cleaned up and textured. A series of PAR 38 halogen recessed fixtures were installed inside the well. The modification afforded the room not only an updated look, but a greater feeling of volume as well.

A ledge was added to the dropped ceiling upon which two halogen desk lamps were placed to provide light to the dining table.

The counter and splash are evenly illuminated with festoon strip lighting. Pinhole spots were used to bring the task areas at the sink and peninsula up to the appropriate footcandle level.

Updating a Fluorescent Dropped Ceiling

The old dropped fluorescent ceilings which used aluminum channels and acrylic panels can give rise to a whole new look as shown in figure 6.26 without any structural renovation.

Figure 6.27   A Soffit Well for Track Lighting

The designer of the kitchen in figure 6.28 has made a wise choice, possibly the only choice, in using track in this room with a steeply vaulted ceiling. The track is mounted on top of the suspended beams. Mono-points can then be directed down as needed to the kitchen below.

Note how the white fixture hides against the white ceiling.

Track Lighting

As I have mentioned earlier, I am no fan of track lighting. There are instances, however, where its use is warranted, if not necessary. Let's look at a few examples of how track fixtures can be used successfully, or at least, with fewer visual repercussions.

When using track lighting, always consider the back drop to the fixtures from the observers point of view. The contrast between the mono-points and the material behind them determines how readily they will be seen.

The kitchen in figure 6.27 tucks the track fixtures up in a soffit well. This is better than having the fixtures drop down into the room where the back-drop might be contrasting cabinetry or wall surface. In my opinion, although in the well, the fixtures still appear "busy."

Figure 6.28   Track Mounted Atop Beam

Chapter 6 — Practical Application

Samuel Kulla, CKD/Marge Brown

Figure 6.29   *Mono-Points Equidistant Above Counter Surfaces*

Mounting all of the lamps at the same distance above the work plane is a solid alternative to installing increasingly more powerful lamps as the vault rises. This also makes it easier for the client to replace lamps. Remember that the greater the distance, the more powerful the lamp will need to be to provide the same amount of light.

In figure 6.29, the minimal style of the fixtures selected, along with the non-contrasting white color, mitigates the aesthetic problems.

Cable lighting is a low voltage system where a transformer feeds two bare cables which are strung parallel across a space using various standoffs and anchors. The cables are then tensioned via turnbuckles.

The lampholders (usually MR16), which can get downright wacky, simply clamp to the cables and complete the circuit.

Notice how cable lights add to the constructionist nature of the design in figure 6.30.

NKBA

Figure 6.30   *Cable Lighting*

Another adaptation of track fixtures is shown in figure 6.31. The 2 x 6 tongue and groove ceiling *is* the roof. There is no attic, no joist space, nothing.

Fortunately the house was being re-roofed during the remodel, so electrical conduit was run on top of the roof and under the shingles. Three inch diameter rough-in boxes were cut into the planking.

Most track manufacturers make a canopy adapter which attaches to the rough in box and allows a standard mono-point to snap into it. It is a kind of trackless track. You have to know where to place the rough-in boxes when using this method because there is no moving them later.

To make the mono-points further disappear, white was chosen to match the ceiling and they were positioned perpendicular to the floor to avoid the dynamic line.

This is an instance where track was indeed the best choice for the lighting job.

Michael De Luca, CKD, ASID   *MDL & A*

Figure 6.31   ***Mono-Point Fixtures Mounted on Canopy Adapters***

Bath Lighting Plan 1

There are some special considerations which must be met when lighting a bath or powder room which differ from the kitchen. For this discussion, refer to figures 6.32 through 6.35.

What we see in figure 6.32 is a two bath conversion from what was once a single guest bathroom. This solution now provides a powder room, as well as a smaller private bath for one of the bedrooms.

These small spaces provide an opportunity to discuss quite a few lighting issues. The first lighting problem for the powder room was that it no longer had access to an outside window. I like any bathroom to have natural light during daylight hours. It has a soothing effect and is energy efficient.

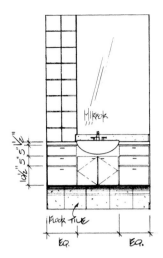

ELEVATION ⑦

Figure 6.33   Glass Block Passive Lighting   *MDL & A*

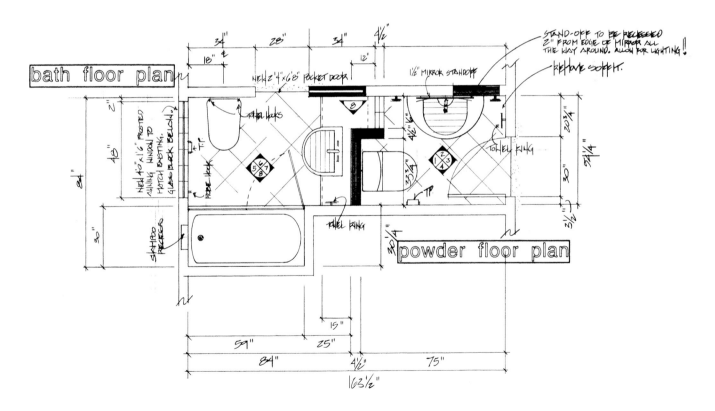

Figure 6.32   Bath 1 Floor Plan   *MDL & A*

The solution to the natural daylight problem for an interior bathroom, in this case, comes through the use of glass block in an area of the wall dividing the two baths. The light is passively "stolen" from the adjacent room. The outside wall of the guest bath has a transom window over a generous area of glass block. The natural light existing in the guest bath is then transmitted to the powder room through the two vertical glass block columns to the left of the guest bath sink. See elevation 7. Obviously the block has to be quite obscure.

The functional portion of the lighting in the powder room is from two wall sconces mounted about eye level on either side of the mirror. The sconces offer frontal lighting which fill the shadows of the face. For applying makeup this is a must.

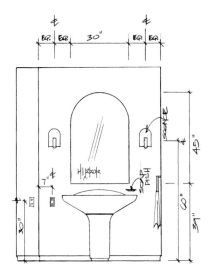

ELEVATION ②

Figure 6.35   Forward Lighting

MDL & A

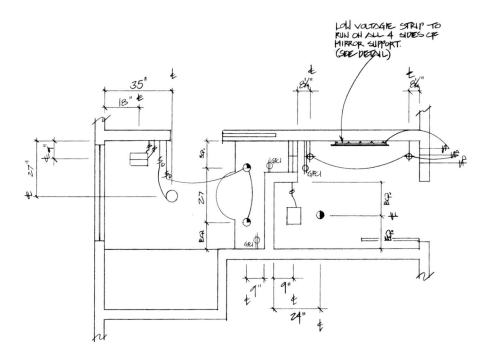

Figure 6.34   Bath 1 Lighting Plan

MDL & A

Notice that the mirror floats 1.5 inches off the wall. Festoon strip lighting is wrapped around the entire perimeter of the standoff. The strip lighting silhouettes the mirror and creates a nice effect. The strip lighting will remain on while entertaining along with the light over the commode which illuminates a vertically oriented piece of art. Guests entering the powder room will switch on the sconces for using the mirror and for general lighting.

The guest bathroom will not be used extensively, so the lighting is strictly functional. Two MR16 cans are used over the pullman counter. I usually place these cans 9 inches off the mirror for the least amount of shadow and equally spaced left to right from the center line of the sink. This will give even illumination to both sides of the face. Ideally, some sort of frontal lighting should have been used.

One centrally located recessed fixture was provided for general lighting and for using the tub/shower. A fixture over the tub itself is a nice touch in larger bathrooms. Remember that special damp location fixtures must be used for tubs and showers, usually with a lens to meet local codes.

Notice the position of the fan in each bath (rectangular symbol). I like to position my exhaust fans as shown for two reasons; the exhaust is located where it is the most useful and many fans are outfitted with a lamp which works well for reading. Another nice feature is a timer switch for the fan which can be set to run unattended for 30 minutes after a shower to reduce mildew growth. This is a good reason to install a fan regardless of the presence of an outside window which may, in winter, remain closed.

Pullman Lighting at Two Sinks

The most important lighting feature you can provide a client in a bathroom is good frontal lighting. For a woman, the recessed area above the eye is filled with light to facilitate applying makeup. For a man, the light fills the shadows under the chin and nose for shaving. Putting contact lenses in is also made easier. Facial fill lighting becomes increasingly important as a person ages.

The problem with wall mounted lighting is that the fixtures can detract from the visually expanding effect of a wall of mirror. Like many things in design, there may be compromise depending on the clients' preferences.

By arranging the sconce fixtures as shown in figure 6.36, the number of fixtures can be reduced. Notice how the center sconce provides illumination to both sinks reducing the fixture count from four to three.

Try to think about the lighting during the design of your bathroom. It will make the lighting design much easier and faster to accomplish... and provide better lighting for the client.

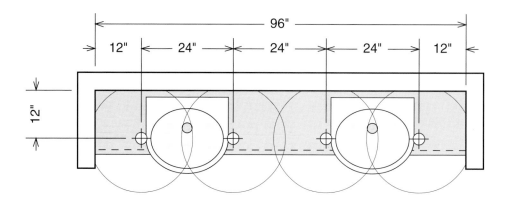

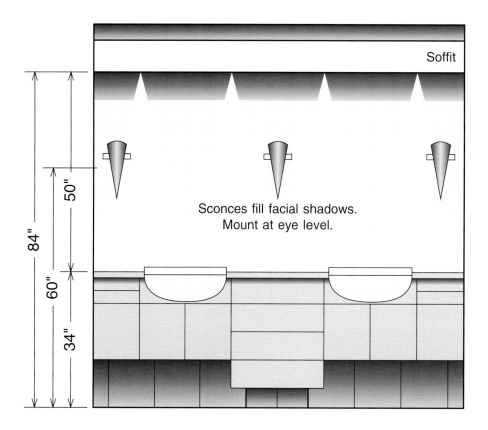

Soffit

Sconces fill facial shadows.
Mount at eye level.

Figure 6.36   Lighting a Double Sink Pullman   *MDL & A*

Bath Lighting Plan 2

The next plan is a large master bath. Mostly, I want you to see how the concepts we have discussed have been implemented into this plan. Also, a legend of the fixtures and lamps used has been provided for you to consider.

This bath was designed for a brick *French Country* home in California where the codes are very stringent regarding the use of fluorescent lighting as general illumination in all kitchens and baths. To accommodate this code, a ledge was created at one end of the bath upon which inexpensive 4 foot fluorescent fixtures were evenly distributed. The light from these lamps is directed upward so that it bounces off the white ceiling providing soft indirect illumination to the room. A center mounted chandelier has been placed where the hip rafters meet the ridge. The vault is a 10/12 pitch.

Low voltage MR16 lamps in 4 inch diameter cans were mounted in a small soffit that runs above all the counter areas. Note the 21 inch spacing repeats over the vanity to maintain a consistant look and function. Sconce fixtures were placed on either side of framed oval mirrors at each sink.

At the vanity, two recessed vertical linestra lamps are used in the mirror at either side of a medicine cabinet for facial fill, see the inset detail on the following page. You will see some examples of this lamp used in upcoming photographs.

Two MR16 cans are also used over the tub for reading and to provide backlighting to the stained glass windows in the bay window. An elegant look from outside the residence.

In the shower a single compact fluorescent recessed can is used (damp location rated).

The commode room was designed with three 42 inch wide areas; commode, bidet, and entry. In designing the room in this manner, the lamps can be centered in each section and maintain the same illumination to the walls.

Again, notice how the fixtures throughout the bath are grouped to create functional, as well as mood lighting.

Daylight is passively provided to the commode room from the etched glass pane at the shower and the etched french door which accesses the skylight.

		MFR.	HOUSING/TRIM	LAMP	DESCRIPTION
○	•	Prescolite	LVH4 LV1C	Q35MR16/FL40° *GE FNW*	• Counter Lighting • Alzak
	•	Robern	MTL 40F 2 Light Kit	Linestra 150W *Osram*	• Vanity Lighting • Cabinet Mounted
Ⓕⓛ	•	Halo	H801 803	F26DBXT4/SPX35 3,500K 82CRI *GE*	• Shower Lighting • Compact Fluorescent
◕	•	Prescolite	PBX TBW15	50PAR30/CAP/FL/40° *Sylvania*	• Commode Lighting • Alzak
▭	•	Lithonia	F40T12 Single Side Mount Tube	F40SPX35 3,500K 82CRI *GE*	• General Lighting • Mount on top of Ledge • See Mounting Detail
FAN	•	Nutone	QT 150 2.5 Sones	N/A	• Ceiling Exhaust Fan

Figure 6.37   ***Bath 2 Legend***   *MDL & A*

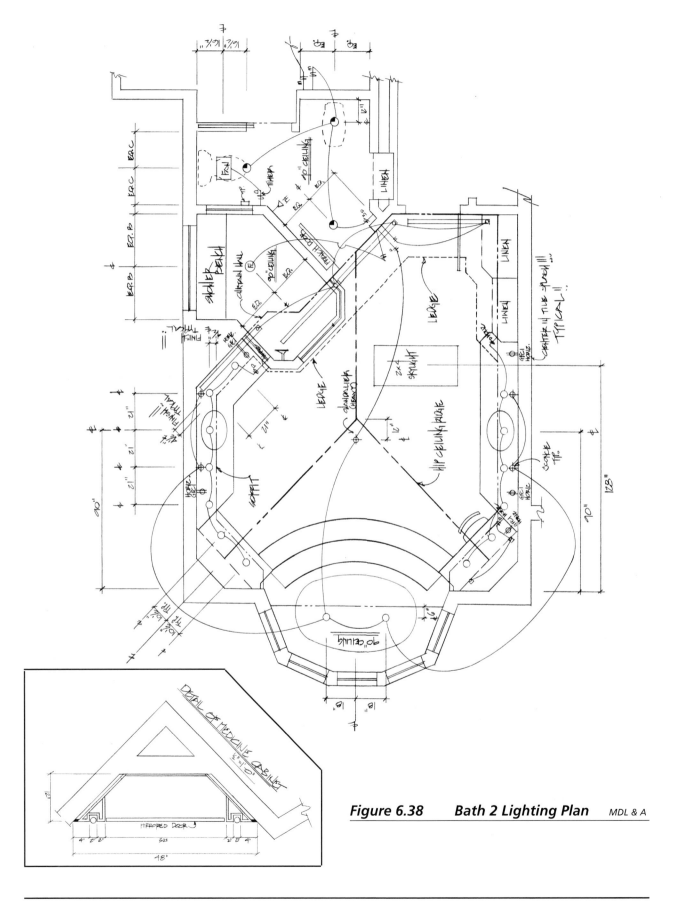

Figure 6.38   **Bath 2 Lighting Plan**   MDL & A

Chapter 6 — Practical Application

Bath Lighting Solutions

The following photographs offer some practical solutions to lighting the bath for utility as well as aesthetics.

The master bath shown in figure 6.39 has the perfect balance of down and fill lighting. The ledge around the perimeter houses recessed cans with alzak trims and the framed mirrors flanked by shaded sconces, all amid a marble backdrop offer traditional elegance.

The illumination provided here is extremely functional. Note the magnifying mirror mounted on an adjustable wall mounted arm at the far left.

Kathleen Donohue, CKD, CBD

Photo David Livingston

Figure 6.39   *Down Lighting with Sconces for Facial Shadow Fill*

NKBA

Figure 6.40 *Down Lighting with Sconces for Facial Shadow Fill*

Figure 6.40 shows another good example of balanced lighting for the bath at a slightly reduced price tag.

The linestra lamps shown in figure 6.41 can be used very successfully in more contemporary situations. Try recessing them in the mirror. A nice touch.

Note the yellow color of the lamp. It is incandescent and therefore warm in color temperature.

One manufacturer has developed a tube within which are placed alternating warm and cool lamps. They look frightful when on, but are very practical. It is best to apply makeup under the same color illumination that you will be seen in. By turning both the warm and cool lamps on, a neutral color is achieved.

Doris Amsterdam *NKBA*

Figure 6.41 *Linestra Lamps*

The bathroom shown in figure 6.42 shows the incandescent linestra lamp in a more traditional setting. Clients have reported that the linestra lamp alone is not adequate for makeup application. Make sure to use properly sized downlighting as well.

Merrie Fredericks, CBD/Phillip Fredericks   *Photo Maura McEvoy*

Figure 6.42   *Linestra in Traditional Setting*

A chandelier over a tub is a thoughtful touch and brings a sense of drama to the room.

Merrie Fredericks, CBD/Phillip Fredericks   *Photo Maura McEvoy*

Figure 6.43   *Chandelier Over Tub*

Tom Trzcinski, CKD, CBD   *Photo Maura McEvoy*

Figure 6.44   ***Theatre Lighting in Fluted Column***

Figure 6.44 shows an interesting application of theatre lighting. The fixture is set in a column flanking the sink. It is best to evenly illuminate the face by using fill lighting on both sides at no more than 3 feet apart.

The vanity shown in figure 6.45 utilizes the oldest lighting arrangement, considered to be the best by many professional makeup artists. The theatre lighting wraps the face with light. The designer here has added a recessed fluorescent ceiling fixture as well with an egg-crate panel for glare reduction.

Try designing your vanities at a 15 inch depth with winged mirrors. The first thing a woman does at a deep vanity counter is to set a small mirror in front of her. The 15 inch depth eliminates the need of a secondary mirror.

I get more referrals from this little trick...

NKBA

Figure 6.45   ***Theater Lighting Traditional Arrangement***

Art Lighting

Most of the information on art lighting is contained in Chapter 7, *Art Lighting*. Invaluable information on fitting the lamp to the art and determining its candlepower is contained there.

The living room depicted in figure 6.46 shows evenly spaced MR16 recessed lighting in a soffit. Three of the fixtures provide downlighting to the sofa. The other two illuminate the galleria wall.

When placing fixtures for a sofa, always place them 36 inches out from the wall (sofa depth). This keeps the halloween shadows off the face. These cans have been outfitted with alzak trims.

The art fixtures use the mirror light trim. An aiming angle of 60° down from the ceiling will provide the most pleasing texture and shadow for art. The footcandle level should be about five times that of the surrounding light. Note that the point of art lighting is the art. Use unobtrusive fixtures and trim.

MR16 is considered the best lighting for art due to its low heat when compared to PAR Lamps.

Michael De Luca, CKD, ASID

Photo Glenn Cormier

Figure 6.46   *Mirror Light on Art Wall with MR16 Open Alzak Recessed Cans Over Sofa*

Miscellaneous

Structural Considerations

Ceiling framing can be anything from 2 x 4 studs to 2 x 16 joists spaced either at 16 inch or 24 inch centers. Obviously, the location of these ceiling members can affect the location of the luminaires. If at all possible, determine the location of the ceiling joists prior to laying out the reflected ceiling plan. In new construction, it is simply a matter of visiting the job site and taking measurements of the exposed joists. Remodeling is a little trickier. By using a density sensitive stud finder, available at most home centers, the location of two joists can be determined which will give the designer a good idea of the construction of the balance of the ceiling.

The procedure goes as follows: locate the first joist by running the stud finder in either direction to determine the direction of the joist; measure this point from a known wall; then move the finder perpendicular to the first joist until the second joist is found; measure the distance between the two and the rest of the joists should follow suit.

Sometimes it is preferable to head out a particular area to allow for a specific lighting layout. Outside of the additional cost, this is a structural change in most cases, and needs to be looked at by an engineer and approved by the local building department.

Another consideration when using recessed lighting is joist height and possible obstructions in the attic or space between floors (i.e., plumbing lines, ducting, etc.).

Often, plumbing lines and ducting can be rerouted, but raising a second story to accommodate lighting isn't a cost-effective solution. There are cans that will fit within a 2 x 8, 2 x 6, and even a 2 x 4 joist height. On the other hand, cans can run to 16 inches in height. Always check specifications.

It is a good idea to add a disclaimer to lighting plans regarding existing framing, especially when access is not possible.

Switching

The wattage rating on the switch is important. If the lighting plan calls for 8, 100 watt lamps, the required rating on the switch will need to be at least 800 watts. A standard switch is rated at 600 watts. A 1000 watt switch is available, but might need to be special ordered. The same applies to dimmer switches.

If two entrances serve a room, use a 3-way switch to control the general lighting at each entrance.

A 3-way switch is one that when used with another 3-way switch, allows on/off control at each switch location. A 4-way switch is used with two other 3-way switches for three or more switch locations. Three-way dimmers are available, but only dim at one location. Determine where the dimming action will most conveniently occur when specifying the dimmer location.

Try to gang switches in groups of 3 or less. People have a hard time remembering which switch controls what when ganging 4 or more. For aesthetic purposes, specify on elevations where 2, 3, and 4 gang switch plates are to be used.

Chapter 6 — Practical Application

There are many styles of dimmers available (toggle, rocker, rocker with on/off switch, etc.) Specify which type is to be used.

It is normal for a dimmer switch to be warm to the touch. If it becomes hot, it is probably underrated for the lighting load.

Stacked switches are configured to use a single gang receptacle trim plate with one switch in each "plug" location. The on/off movement is left and right for these switches. They work well in a pinch, but, again, are difficult for people to remember whether right or left is "on" as opposed to the usual up and down. Of course, if mounted horizontally, the on/off movement becomes up and down.

Pocket doors do not allow enough depth for a switch box to be installed. When using a pocket door, consider alternate switch locations.

When using dimmers with any lamp, remember that color temperature is a function of voltage. A dimmer reduces voltage to the lamp, thereby reducing the kelvin temperature and causing a warmer rendition than the specifications would otherwise indicate for the lamp.

When using low-voltage lighting, where the transformer is not part of the luminaire, be sure to show the transformer in the lighting plan and its relationship to the switch for the lighting circuit. Also, make a note to the electrician to check manufacturers' specifications for wire gauge. Some electricians, with little low voltage lighting experience, assume that standard, small gauge, low voltage, bell wire will suffice. In reality, most low voltage circuits will, at least, require 12 gauge stranded wiring. The longer the run from the transformer and the greater the number of lights on the circuit, the heavier the gauge will need to be.

When dimming low-voltage lighting, a special low voltage dimmer will need to be specified. This is the electrician's responsibility. However, it is good practice to make a note on the plans.

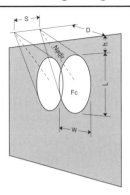

CHAPTER 7

ART LIGHTING

Art lighting is fairly simple if you keep a few very important fundamentals in mind:

- **Aiming Angle**

- **Relative FootCandle Level**

- **Subject Coverage**

- **Fixture Selection**

Preferred Aiming Angle

The preferred aiming angle to minimize reflected glare is 60° measured from the ceiling down. The chart, figure 7.1, indicates where to place the fixture to achieve 60°, 45°, and 30° at various ceiling heights.

Typically, the dimension off the floor to center of the art for best viewing is at eye level, approximately 66 inches. Using the chart, a fixture placed in an 8 foot ceiling at 60° to the art wall will need to be located 18 inches out from the wall (a distance of 18 inches), 30 inches at 45°, and 54 inches at 30°.

Obviously, art is placed at positions other than eye level for aesthetic effect or when placing framed works in a group. In this case, nadir should be at the center of the piece and at a 60° angle when possible.

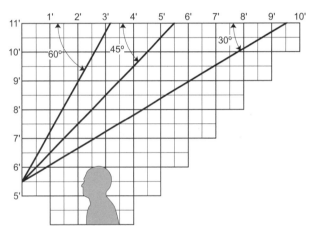

Figure 7.1   Distance Finding Grid

Relative Footcandle Level

The goal of art lighting is to provide highlight or accent. In order to do this, the footcandle level must be five times that of the ambient (surrounding) light. If a painting is to be accented in a living room where the ambient light level is known to be 10 Fc, then the Fc level on the painting will need to be 50 Fc. In a kitchen or bath with a general lighting level of 40 Fc, the art lighting will need to provide the same painting with 200 Fc to have the same effect as in the living room. It is the 5:1 ratio that creates the illusion of highlight.

For kitchens, since art will most likely be viewed when the general lighting has been dimmed for effect, figure the general lighting Fc level at 50% when determining the 5:1 ratio. For the example above, 20 Fc (50% of 40 Fc) will result in a 100 Fc art level. A more realistic approach.

Subject Coverage

When a lamp is aimed at an angle, the beam pattern on the wall will become an ellipse. The dimension of the ellipse will depend on the distance the lamp is mounted from the wall and the aiming angle, as well as, the beam angle of the lamp.

The tables on the following pages will give the width (W) and length (L) as well as the dimension from the ellipse to the ceiling (h) for each of the three aiming angles, figure 7.2. The goal is to find a lamp that will cover the subject matter in both dimensions while providing an adequate footcandle (Fc) level at Nadir.

When a single lamp can't be found to cover the width of the art, two or more fixtures mounted parallel with the wall may be needed. Generally, the ellipse width (W) is considered the maximum spacing (S) to the next fixture. It is recommended to provide some overlap here as well.

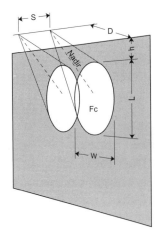

Figure 7.2   *Ellipse Shape & Position*

Fixture Selection

In addition to finding a lamp that will produce adequate coverage and intensity, the fixture which houses the lamp should serve two purposes. The first, to accommodate the lamp while providing the prescribed aiming angle, the second is to be as unobtrusive as the situation dictates.

In a foyer or dining room, a chandelier can become a part of the focal point. For art lighting however, the light fixture can detract from the subject at hand.

I can think of no situation, when viewing art, where the distraction of the fixture itself is a desired element. The ideal is to select a fixture that becomes as invisible as possible. The oval slot or mirror light trims, described in Chapter 5, are both good examples of subtle fixtures which do not compete for the viewers attention.

What, then, makes a fixture unobtrusive? Bear in mind the elements of design and how they attract the eye. Contrast, dynamic line, break in plane, and saturated color all serve to draw the viewers attention. Avoid all these to make a fixture virtually disappear.

Ironically, track fixtures, which are so often used for art lighting, are the worst offenders. Both the track and the mono-point, break plane with the ceiling. The mono-points are aimed at an angle (dynamic line) and multiple fixtures add multiple confusion. Finally, most mono-points are outfitted with a black step-baffle trim which contrasts with the fixture, if not the ceiling.

Remember, the art is the point of the illumination.

Beam Angle

Distance	W	L	h	W	L	h	W	L	h	W	L	h	W	L	h	W	L	h
	1°			5°			10°			15°			20°			25°		
1'	0"	1"	20"	2"	4"	19"	4"	9"	17"	6"	13"	16"	8"	19"	14"	11"	25"	13"
1.5'	1"	1"	31"	3"	6"	28"	6"	13"	26"	9"	20"	23"	13"	28"	21"	16"	37"	20"
2'	1"	2"	41"	4"	8"	38"	8"	17"	34"	13"	27"	31"	17"	37"	29"	21"	50"	26"
2.5'	1"	2"	51"	5"	11"	47"	10"	21"	43"	16"	33"	39"	21"	47"	36"	27"	62"	33"
3'	1"	3"	61"	6"	13"	57"	13"	26"	51"	19"	40"	47"	25"	56"	43"	32"	75"	39"
3.5'	1"	3"	71"	7"	15"	66"	15"	30"	60"	22"	47"	55"	30"	65"	50"	37"	87"	46"
4'	2"	3"	81"	8"	17"	75"	17"	34"	69"	25"	53"	63"	34"	75"	57"	43"	100"	52"
4.5'	2"	4"	92"	9"	19"	85"	19"	39"	77"	28"	60"	70"	38"	84"	64"	48"	112"	59"
5'	2"	4"	102"	10"	21"	94"	21"	43"	86"	32"	67"	78"	42"	93"	72"	53"	125"	65"
5.5'	2"	5"	112"	12"	23"	104"	23"	47"	94"	35"	73"	86"	47"	103"	79"	59"	137"	72"
6'	3"	5"	122"	13"	25"	113"	25"	52"	103"	38"	80"	94"	51"	112"	86"	64"	150"	79"
6.5'	3"	5"	132"	14"	27"	122"	27"	56"	111"	41"	87"	102"	55"	121"	93"	69"	162"	85"
7'	3"	6"	143"	15"	30"	132"	29"	60"	120"	44"	93"	109"	59"	131"	100"	74"	175"	92"
7.5'	3"	6"	153"	16"	32"	141"	31"	64"	129"	47"	100"	117"	63"	140"	107"	80"	187"	98"
8'	3"	7"	163"	17"	34"	151"	34"	69"	137"	51"	107"	125"	68"	149"	114"	85"	200"	105"
8.5'	4"	7"	173"	18"	36"	160"	36"	73"	146"	54"	113"	133"	72"	159"	122"	90"	212"	111"
9'	4"	8"	183"	19"	38"	170"	38"	77"	154"	57"	120"	141"	76"	168"	129"	96"	225"	118"
9.5'	4"	8"	194"	20"	40"	179"	40"	82"	163"	60"	127"	149"	80"	177"	136"	101"	237"	124"
10'	4"	8"	204"	21"	42"	188"	42"	86"	171"	63"	133"	156"	85"	187"	143"	106"	250"	131"

Figure 7.3   **Beam Width, Length, and Dimension from Ceiling at 60° Aiming Angle**

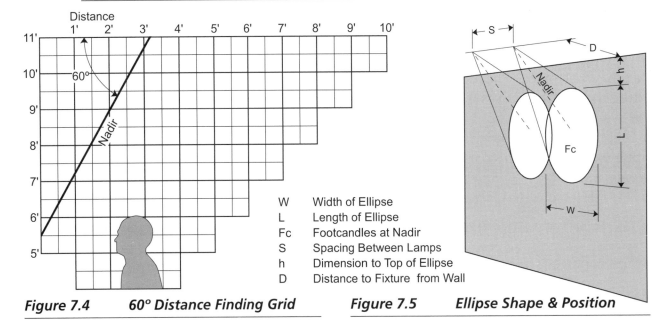

W   Width of Ellipse
L   Length of Ellipse
Fc   Footcandles at Nadir
S   Spacing Between Lamps
h   Dimension to Top of Ellipse
D   Distance to Fixture from Wall

Figure 7.4   **60° Distance Finding Grid**

Figure 7.5   **Ellipse Shape & Position**

Figure 7.6

60° Aiming Angle

Find the candlepower for desired footcandle level at a given distance.

Footcandle Level

Distance	1Fc	5Fc	10Fc	15Fc	20Fc	25Fc	30Fc	35Fc	40Fc	45Fc	50Fc
1'	8	40	80	120	160	200	240	280	320	360	400
1.5'	18	90	180	270	360	450	540	630	720	810	900
2'	32	160	320	480	640	800	960	1,120	1,280	1,440	1,600
2.5'	50	250	500	750	1,000	1,250	1,500	1,750	2,000	2,250	2,500
3'	72	360	720	1,080	1,440	1,800	2,160	2,520	2,880	3,240	3,600
3.5'	98	490	980	1,470	1,960	2,450	2,940	3,430	3,920	4,410	4,900
4'	128	640	1,280	1,920	2,560	3,200	3,840	4,480	5,120	5,760	6,400
4.5'	162	810	1,620	2,430	3,240	4,050	4,860	5,670	6,480	7,290	8,100
5'	200	1,000	2,000	3,000	4,000	5,000	6,000	7,000	8,000	9,000	10,000
5.5'	242	1,210	2,420	3,630	4,840	6,050	7,260	8,470	9,680	10,890	12,100
6'	288	1,440	2,880	4,320	5,760	7,200	8,640	10,080	11,520	12,960	14,400
6.5'	338	1,690	3,380	5,070	6,760	8,450	10,140	11,830	13,520	15,210	16,900
7'	392	1,960	3,920	5,880	7,840	9,800	11,760	13,720	15,680	17,640	19,600
7.5'	450	2,250	4,500	6,750	9,000	11,250	13,500	15,750	18,000	20,250	22,500
8'	512	2,560	5,120	7,680	10,240	12,800	15,360	17,920	20,480	23,040	25,600
8.5'	578	2,890	5,780	8,670	11,560	14,450	17,340	20,230	23,120	26,010	28,900
9'	648	3,240	6,480	9,720	12,960	16,200	19,440	22,680	25,920	29,160	
9.5'	722	3,610	7,220	10,830	14,440	18,050	21,660	25,270	28,880		
10'	800	4,000	8,000	12,000	16,000	20,000	24,000	28,000			

Δ ——————— **Candlepower** ——————— Δ

Beam Angle

W	L	h	W	L	h	W	L	h	W	L	h	W	L	h	W	L	h	Distance
	30º			35º			40º			45º			50º			55º		
13''	33''	12''	15''	43''	11''	17''	58''	10''	20''	82''	9''	22''	129''	8''	25''	267''	8''	1'
19''	49''	18''	23''	65''	16''	26''	87''	15''	30''	123''	14''	34''	193''	13''	37''	401''	11''	1.5'
26''	66''	24''	30''	86''	22''	35''	116''	20''	40''	164''	18''	45''	258''	17''	50''	534''	15''	2'
32''	82''	30''	38''	108''	27''	44''	145''	25''	50''	205''	23''	56''	322''	21''	62''	668''	19''	2.5'
39''	98''	36''	45''	129''	33''	52''	174''	30''	60''	246''	28''	67''	386''	25''	75''	802''	23''	3'
45''	115''	42''	53''	151''	38''	61''	203''	35''	70''	287''	32''	78''	451''	29''	87''	935''	27''	3.5'
51''	131''	48''	61''	173''	44''	70''	232''	40''	80''	328''	37''	90''	515''	34''	100''	1069''	31''	4'
58''	148''	54''	68''	194''	49''	79''	261''	45''	89''	369''	41''	101''	579''	38''	112''	1202''	34''	4.5'
64''	164''	60''	76''	216''	55''	87''	290''	50''	99''	410''	46''	112''	644''	42''	125''	1336''	38''	5'
71''	180''	66''	83''	237''	60''	96''	319''	55''	109''	451''	51''	123''	708''	46''	137''	1470''	42''	5.5'
77''	197''	72''	91''	259''	66''	105''	348''	60''	119''	492''	55''	134''	773''	50''	150''	1603''	46''	6'
84''	213''	78''	98''	280''	71''	114''	377''	65''	129''	533''	60''	145''	837''	55''	162''	1737''	50''	6.5'
90''	229''	84''	106''	302''	77''	122''	406''	70''	139''	574''	64''	157''	901''	59''	175''	1870''	54''	7'
96''	246''	90''	114''	323''	82''	131''	435''	76''	149''	615''	69''	168''	966''	63''	187''	2004''	57''	7.5'
103''	262''	96''	121''	345''	88''	140''	464''	81''	159''	656''	74''	179''	1030''	67''	200''	2138''	61''	8'
109''	279''	102''	129''	367''	93''	148''	493''	86''	169''	696''	78''	190''	1094''	71''	212''	2271''	65''	8.5'
116''	295''	108''	136''	388''	99''	157''	522''	91''	179''	737''	83''	201''	1159''	76''	225''	2405''	69''	9'
122''	311''	114''	144''	410''	104''	166''	551''	96''	189''	778''	87''	213''	1223''	80''	237''	2538''	73''	9.5'
129''	328''	120''	151''	431''	110''	175''	580''	101''	199''	819''	92''	224''	1288''	84''	250''	2672''	76''	10'

Art Lighting for 60° Aiming Angle

Step 1: Find the fixture distance for the ceiling height. Figure 7.4

Step 2: Using the distance found in Step 1, find the candlepower needed to provide the desired footcandle level (Fc). Figure 7.6

Note: The Fc level should be 5 times the ambient light level.

Step 3: Again using the distance found in Step 1, find the width (W) of the beam ellipse that fits the width of the art. Then read up the column to find the beam angle. Figure 7.3

If the artwork is too wide, find a beam angle that will cover half the width and use two lamps, etc., until the width of the art is covered. Spacing (S) should be at least the ellipse width (W), allow some intersect if possible.

Step 4: Make sure that the length (L) of the ellipse will cover the height of the artwork and note the distance from the ceiling to the top of the ellipse (h). Figure 7.3

Note: The width (W) of the ellipse will always be centered on the point where nadir meets the wall, but the length (L) of the ellipse will not. Use (h) to locate the top of the ellipse from the ceiling to make sure the height of the artwork is properly illuminated.

Step 5: Go to Appendix A to locate a lamp with the candlepower found in Step 2 and the beam angle found in Step 3.

The procedure for 45° and 30° aiming angles on the following pages is the same.

Footcandle Level

55Fc	60Fc	65Fc	70Fc	75Fc	80Fc	85Fc	90Fc	95Fc	100Fc	200Fc	Distance
440	480	520	560	600	640	680	720	760	800	1,600	1'
990	1,080	1,170	1,260	1,350	1,440	1,530	1,620	1,710	1,800	3,600	1.5'
1,760	1,920	2,080	2,240	2,400	2,560	2,720	2,880	3,040	3,200	6,400	2'
2,750	3,000	3,250	3,500	3,750	4,000	4,250	4,500	4,750	5,000	10,000	2.5'
3,960	4,320	4,680	5,040	5,400	5,760	6,120	6,480	6,840	7,200	14,400	3'
5,390	5,880	6,370	6,860	7,350	7,840	8,330	8,820	9,310	9,800	19,600	3.5'
7,040	7,680	8,320	8,960	9,600	10,240	10,880	11,520	12,160	12,800	25,600	4'
8,910	9,720	10,530	11,340	12,150	12,960	13,770	14,580	15,390	16,200		4.5'
11,000	12,000	13,000	14,000	15,000	16,000	17,000	18,000	19,000	20,000		5'
13,310	14,520	15,730	16,940	18,150	19,360	20,570	21,780	22,990	24,200		5.5'
15,840	17,280	18,720	20,160	21,600	23,040	24,480	25,920	27,360	28,800		6'
18,590	20,280	21,970	23,660	25,350	27,040	28,730					6.5'
21,560	23,520	25,480	27,440	29,400							7'
24,750	27,000	29,250									7.5'
28,160											8'
											8.5'
											9'
											9.5'
											10'

Δ ——— **Candlepower** ——— Δ

60°
Aiming
Angle

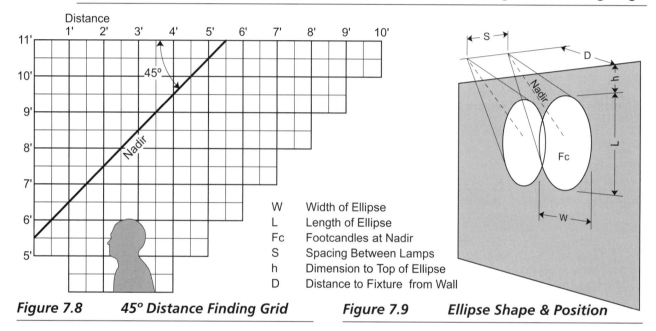

Beam Angle

Distance	W	L	h	W	L	h	W	L	h	W	L	h	W	L	h	W	L	h
		1º			5º			10º			15º			20º			25º	
1'	0''	0''	12''	1''	2''	11''	3''	4''	10''	4''	6''	9''	6''	9''	8''	8''	11''	8''
1.5'	0''	1''	18''	2''	3''	16''	4''	6''	15''	7''	10''	14''	9''	13''	13''	11''	17''	11''
2'	1''	1''	24''	3''	4''	22''	6''	8''	20''	9''	13''	18''	12''	17''	17''	15''	22''	15''
2.5'	1''	1''	29''	4''	5''	27''	7''	11''	25''	11''	16''	23''	15''	22''	21''	19''	28''	19''
3'	1''	1''	35''	4''	6''	33''	9''	13''	30''	13''	19''	28''	18''	26''	25''	23''	34''	23''
3.5'	1''	1''	41''	5''	7''	38''	10''	15''	35''	16''	23''	32''	21''	31''	29''	26''	39''	27''
4'	1''	2''	47''	6''	8''	44''	12''	17''	40''	18''	26''	37''	24''	35''	34''	30''	45''	31''
4.5'	1''	2''	53''	7''	9''	49''	13''	19''	45''	20''	29''	41''	27''	39''	38''	34''	50''	34''
5'	1''	2''	59''	7''	10''	55''	15''	21''	50''	22''	32''	46''	30''	44''	42''	38''	56''	38''
5.5'	2''	2''	65''	8''	12''	60''	16''	23''	55''	25''	35''	51''	33''	48''	46''	41''	62''	42''
6'	2''	3''	71''	9''	13''	66''	18''	25''	60''	27''	39''	55''	36''	52''	50''	45''	67''	46''
6.5'	2''	3''	77''	10''	14''	71''	19''	28''	65''	29''	42''	60''	39''	57''	55''	49''	73''	50''
7'	2''	3''	83''	10''	15''	77''	21''	30''	70''	31''	45''	64''	42''	61''	59''	53''	78''	54''
7.5'	2''	3''	88''	11''	16''	82''	22''	32''	76''	34''	48''	69''	45''	66''	63''	56''	84''	57''
8'	2''	3''	94''	12''	17''	88''	24''	34''	81''	36''	51''	74''	48''	70''	67''	60''	90''	61''
8.5'	3''	4''	100''	13''	18''	93''	25''	36''	86''	38''	55''	78''	51''	74''	71''	64''	95''	65''
9'	3''	4''	106''	13''	19''	99''	27''	38''	91''	40''	58''	83''	54''	79''	76''	68''	101''	69''
9.5'	3''	4''	112''	14''	20''	104''	28''	40''	96''	42''	61''	87''	57''	83''	80''	71''	106''	73''
10'	3''	4''	118''	15''	21''	110''	30''	42''	101''	45''	64''	92''	60''	87''	84''	75''	112''	76''

Figure 7.7   **Beam Width, Length, and Dimension from Ceiling at 45° Aiming Angle**

Figure 7.8   **45° Distance Finding Grid**

W   Width of Ellipse
L   Length of Ellipse
Fc   Footcandles at Nadir
S   Spacing Between Lamps
h   Dimension to Top of Ellipse
D   Distance to Fixture from Wall

Figure 7.9   **Ellipse Shape & Position**

Figure 7.10

45° Aiming Angle

Find the candlepower for desired footcandle level at a given distance.

Footcandle Level

Distance	1Fc	5Fc	10Fc	15Fc	20Fc	25Fc	30Fc	35Fc	40Fc	45Fc	50Fc
1'	3	14	28	42	57	71	85	99	113	127	141
1.5'	6	32	64	95	127	159	191	223	255	286	318
2'	11	57	113	170	226	283	339	396	453	509	566
2.5'	18	88	177	265	354	442	530	619	707	795	884
3'	25	127	255	382	509	636	764	891	1,018	1,146	1,273
3.5'	35	173	346	520	693	866	1,039	1,213	1,386	1,559	1,732
4'	45	226	453	679	905	1,131	1,358	1,584	1,810	2,036	2,263
4.5'	57	286	573	859	1,146	1,432	1,718	2,005	2,291	2,577	2,864
5'	71	354	707	1,061	1,414	1,768	2,121	2,475	2,828	3,182	3,536
5.5'	86	428	856	1,283	1,711	2,139	2,567	2,995	3,422	3,850	4,278
6'	102	509	1,018	1,527	2,036	2,546	3,055	3,564	4,073	4,582	5,091
6.5'	120	598	1,195	1,793	2,390	2,988	3,585	4,183	4,780	5,378	5,975
7'	139	693	1,386	2,079	2,772	3,465	4,158	4,851	5,544	6,237	6,930
7.5'	159	795	1,591	2,386	3,182	3,977	4,773	5,568	6,364	7,159	7,955
8'	181	905	1,810	2,715	3,620	4,525	5,431	6,336	7,241	8,146	9,051
8.5'	204	1,022	2,044	3,065	4,087	5,109	6,131	7,152	8,174	9,196	10,218
9'	229	1,146	2,291	3,437	4,582	5,728	6,873	8,019	9,164	10,310	11,455
9.5'	255	1,276	2,553	3,829	5,105	6,382	7,658	8,934	10,211	11,487	12,763
10'	283	1,414	2,828	4,243	5,657	7,071	8,485	9,899	11,314	12,728	14,142

Δ ——————— **Candlepower** ——————— Δ

Beam Angle

W	L	h	W	L	h	W	L	h	W	L	h	W	L	h	W	L	h	Distance
30°			35°			40°			45°			50°			55°			
9"	14"	7"	11"	17"	6"	12"	20"	6"	14"	24"	5"	16"	29"	4"	18"	34"	4"	1'
14"	21"	10"	16"	25"	9"	19"	30"	8"	21"	36"	7"	24"	43"	7"	27"	51"	6"	1.5'
18"	28"	14"	21"	34"	12"	25"	40"	11"	28"	48"	10"	32"	57"	9"	35"	69"	8"	2'
23"	35"	17"	27"	42"	16"	31"	50"	14"	35"	60"	12"	40"	72"	11"	44"	86"	9"	2.5'
27"	42"	21"	32"	50"	19"	37"	60"	17"	42"	72"	15"	47"	86"	13"	53"	103"	11"	3'
32"	48"	24"	37"	59"	22"	43"	70"	20"	49"	84"	17"	55"	100"	15"	62"	120"	13"	3.5'
36"	55"	28"	43"	67"	25"	49"	81"	22"	56"	96"	20"	63"	114"	17"	71"	137"	15"	4'
41"	62"	31"	48"	76"	28"	56"	91"	25"	63"	108"	22"	71"	129"	20"	80"	154"	17"	4.5'
45"	69"	35"	54"	84"	31"	62"	101"	28"	70"	120"	25"	79"	143"	22"	88"	171"	19"	5'
50"	76"	38"	59"	92"	34"	68"	111"	31"	77"	132"	27"	87"	157"	24"	97"	189"	21"	5.5'
55"	83"	42"	64"	101"	37"	74"	121"	34"	84"	144"	30"	95"	172"	26"	106"	206"	23"	6'
59"	90"	45"	70"	109"	41"	80"	131"	36"	91"	156"	32"	103"	186"	28"	115"	223"	25"	6.5'
64"	97"	48"	75"	118"	44"	86"	141"	39"	98"	168"	35"	111"	200"	31"	124"	240"	26"	7'
68"	104"	52"	80"	126"	47"	93"	151"	42"	105"	180"	37"	119"	215"	33"	133"	257"	28"	7.5'
73"	111"	55"	86"	134"	50"	99"	161"	45"	112"	192"	40"	127"	229"	35"	141"	274"	30"	8'
77"	118"	59"	91"	143"	53"	105"	171"	48"	120"	204"	42"	135"	243"	37"	150"	291"	32"	8.5'
82"	125"	62"	96"	151"	56"	111"	181"	50"	127"	216"	45"	142"	257"	39"	159"	308"	34"	9'
86"	132"	66"	102"	160"	59"	117"	191"	53"	134"	228"	47"	150"	272"	41"	168"	326"	36"	9.5'
91"	139"	69"	107"	168"	62"	124"	201"	56"	141"	240"	50"	158"	286"	44"	177"	343"	38"	10'

Art Lighting for 45° Aiming Angle

Step 1: Find the fixture distance for the ceiling height. Figure 7.8

Step 2: Using the distance found in step 1, find the candlepower needed to provide the desired footcandle level (Fc). Figure 7.10

Note: The Fc level should be 5 times the ambient light level.

Step 3: Again using the distance found in step 1, find the width (W) of the beam ellipse that fits the width of the art. Then read up the column to find the beam angle. Figure 7.7

If the artwork is too wide, find a beam angle that will cover half the width and use two lamps, etc., until the width of the art is covered. Spacing (S) should be at least the ellipse width (W), allow some intersect if possible.

Step 4: Make sure that the length (L) of the ellipse will cover the height of the artwork and note the distance from the ceiling to the top of the ellipse (h). Figure 7.7

Note: The width (W) of the ellipse will always be centered on the point where nadir meets the wall, but the length (L) of the ellipse will not. Use (h) to locate the top of the ellipse from the ceiling to make sure the height of the artwork is properly illuminated.

Step 5: Go to Appendix A to locate a lamp with the candlepower found in step 2 and the beam angle found in step 3.

The procedure for 30° aiming angle on the following pages is the same.

Footcandle Level

55Fc	60Fc	65Fc	70Fc	75Fc	80Fc	85Fc	90Fc	95Fc	100Fc	200Fc	Distance
156	170	184	198	212	226	240	255	269	283	566	1'
350	382	414	445	477	509	541	573	605	636	1,273	1.5'
622	679	735	792	849	905	962	1,018	1,075	1,131	2,263	2'
972	1,061	1,149	1,237	1,326	1,414	1,503	1,591	1,679	1,768	3,536	2.5'
1,400	1,527	1,655	1,782	1,909	2,036	2,164	2,291	2,418	2,546	5,091	3'
1,906	2,079	2,252	2,425	2,599	2,772	2,945	3,118	3,292	3,465	6,930	3.5'
2,489	2,715	2,942	3,168	3,394	3,620	3,847	4,073	4,299	4,525	9,051	4'
3,150	3,437	3,723	4,009	4,296	4,582	4,868	5,155	5,441	5,728	11,455	4.5'
3,889	4,243	4,596	4,950	5,303	5,657	6,010	6,364	6,718	7,071	14,142	5'
4,706	5,134	5,561	5,989	6,417	6,845	7,273	7,700	8,128	8,556	17,112	5.5'
5,600	6,109	6,619	7,128	7,637	8,146	8,655	9,164	9,673	10,182	20,365	6'
6,573	7,170	7,768	8,365	8,963	9,560	10,158	10,755	11,353	11,950	23,900	6.5'
7,623	8,316	9,009	9,702	10,394	11,087	11,780	12,473	13,166	13,859	27,719	7'
8,750	9,546	10,341	11,137	11,932	12,728	13,523	14,319	15,114	15,910		7.5'
9,956	10,861	11,766	12,671	13,576	14,482	15,387	16,292	17,197	18,102		8'
11,239	12,261	13,283	14,305	15,327	16,348	17,370	18,392	19,414	20,435		8.5'
12,601	13,746	14,892	16,037	17,183	18,328	19,474	20,619	21,765	22,910		9'
14,040	15,316	16,592	17,869	19,145	20,421	21,698	22,974	24,250	25,527		9.5'
15,556	16,971	18,385	19,799	21,213	22,627	24,042	25,456	26,870	28,284		10'

Δ ——— Candlepower ——— Δ

45° Aiming Angle

Beam Angle

Distance	1° W	L	h	5° W	L	h	10° W	L	h	15° W	L	h	20° W	L	h	25° W	L	h
1'	0"	0"	7"	1"	1"	6"	2"	3"	6"	4"	4"	5"	5"	6"	4"	6"	7"	4"
1.5'	0"	0"	10"	2"	2"	9"	4"	4"	8"	5"	6"	7"	7"	9"	7"	9"	11"	6"
2'	0"	1"	14"	2"	3"	12"	5"	6"	11"	7"	8"	10"	10"	11"	9"	12"	14"	8"
2.5'	1"	1"	17"	3"	3"	16"	6"	7"	14"	9"	11"	12"	12"	14"	11"	15"	18"	9"
3'	1"	1"	20"	4"	4"	19"	7"	8"	17"	11"	13"	15"	15"	17"	13"	18"	22"	11"
3.5'	1"	1"	24"	4"	5"	22"	8"	10"	20"	13"	15"	17"	17"	20"	15"	22"	25"	13"
4'	1"	1"	27"	5"	6"	25"	10"	11"	22"	15"	17"	20"	20"	23"	17"	25"	29"	15"
4.5'	1"	1"	31"	5"	6"	28"	11"	13"	25"	16"	19"	22"	22"	26"	20"	28"	32"	17"
5'	1"	1"	34"	6"	7"	31"	12"	14"	28"	18"	21"	25"	24"	29"	22"	31"	36"	19"
5.5'	1"	2"	37"	7"	8"	34"	13"	15"	31"	20"	23"	27"	27"	31"	24"	34"	40"	21"
6'	1"	2"	41"	7"	8"	37"	15"	17"	34"	22"	25"	30"	29"	34"	26"	37"	43"	23"
6.5'	2"	2"	44"	8"	9"	41"	16"	18"	36"	24"	28"	32"	32"	37"	28"	40"	47"	25"
7'	2"	2"	48"	8"	10"	44"	17"	20"	39"	26"	30"	35"	34"	40"	31"	43"	50"	26"
7.5'	2"	2"	51"	9"	10"	47"	18"	21"	42"	27"	32"	37"	37"	43"	33"	46"	54"	28"
8'	2"	2"	54"	10"	11"	50"	19"	22"	45"	29"	34"	40"	39"	46"	35"	49"	58"	30"
8.5'	2"	2"	58"	10"	12"	53"	21"	24"	48"	31"	36"	42"	42"	48"	37"	52"	61"	32"
9'	2"	3"	61"	11"	13"	56"	22"	25"	50"	33"	38"	45"	44"	51"	39"	55"	65"	34"
9.5'	2"	3"	64"	11"	13"	59"	23"	27"	53"	35"	40"	47"	46"	54"	41"	58"	69"	36"
10'	2"	3"	68"	12"	14"	62"	24"	28"	56"	36"	42"	50"	49"	57"	44"	61"	72"	38"

Figure 7.11   Beam Width, Length, and Dimension from Ceiling at 30° Aiming Angle

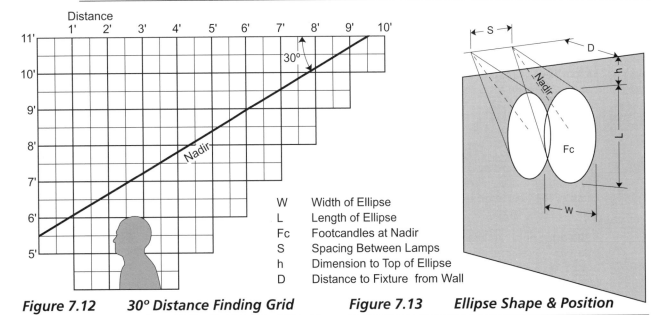

Figure 7.12   30° Distance Finding Grid

W   Width of Ellipse
L   Length of Ellipse
Fc Footcandles at Nadir
S   Spacing Between Lamps
h   Dimension to Top of Ellipse
D   Distance to Fixture from Wall

Figure 7.13   Ellipse Shape & Position

Figure 7.14

30° Aiming Angle

Find the candlepower for desired footcandle level at a given distance.

Footcandle Level

Distance	1Fc	5Fc	10Fc	15Fc	20Fc	25Fc	30Fc	35Fc	40Fc	45Fc	50Fc
1'	2	8	15	23	31	38	46	54	62	69	77
1.5'	3	17	35	52	69	87	104	121	139	156	173
2'	6	31	62	92	123	154	185	216	246	277	308
2.5'	10	48	96	144	192	241	289	337	385	433	481
3'	14	69	139	208	277	346	416	485	554	624	693
3.5'	19	94	189	283	377	472	566	660	754	849	943
4'	25	123	246	370	493	616	739	862	985	1,109	1,232
4.5'	31	156	312	468	624	779	935	1,091	1,247	1,403	1,559
5'	38	192	385	577	770	962	1,155	1,347	1,540	1,732	1,925
5.5'	47	233	466	699	931	1,164	1,397	1,630	1,863	2,096	2,329
6'	55	277	554	831	1,109	1,386	1,663	1,940	2,217	2,494	2,771
6.5'	65	325	650	976	1,301	1,626	1,951	2,277	2,602	2,927	3,252
7'	75	377	754	1,132	1,509	1,886	2,263	2,640	3,018	3,395	3,772
7.5'	87	433	866	1,299	1,732	2,165	2,598	3,031	3,464	3,897	4,330
8'	99	493	985	1,478	1,971	2,463	2,956	3,449	3,941	4,434	4,927
8.5'	111	556	1,112	1,669	2,225	2,781	3,337	3,893	4,449	5,006	5,562
9'	125	624	1,247	1,871	2,494	3,118	3,741	4,365	4,988	5,612	6,235
9.5'	139	695	1,389	2,084	2,779	3,474	4,168	4,863	5,558	6,253	6,947
10'	154	770	1,540	2,309	3,079	3,849	4,619	5,389	6,158	6,928	7,698

Δ ———— **Candlepower** ———— Δ

Beam Angle

W	L	h	W	L	h	W	L	h	W	L	h	W	L	h	W	L	h	Distance
30°			35°			40°			45°			50°			55°			
7"	9"	3"	9"	10"	3"	10"	12"	2"	11"	14"	2"	13"	16"	1"	14"	18"	1"	1'
11"	13"	5"	13"	16"	4"	15"	18"	3"	17"	21"	2"	19"	24"	2"	22"	27"	1"	1.5'
15"	18"	6"	17"	21"	5"	20"	24"	4"	23"	28"	3"	26"	32"	2"	29"	37"	1"	2'
19"	22"	8"	22"	26"	7"	25"	30"	5"	29"	35"	4"	32"	40"	3"	36"	46"	1"	2.5'
22"	26"	10"	26"	31"	8"	30"	37"	6"	34"	42"	5"	39"	48"	3"	43"	55"	2"	3'
26"	31"	11"	31"	37"	9"	35"	43"	7"	40"	49"	6"	45"	56"	4"	50"	64"	2"	3.5'
30"	35"	13"	35"	42"	11"	40"	49"	8"	46"	56"	6"	52"	64"	4"	58"	73"	2"	4'
33"	40"	14"	39"	47"	12"	45"	55"	10"	52"	63"	7"	58"	72"	5"	65"	82"	2"	4.5'
37"	44"	16"	44"	52"	13"	50"	61"	11"	57"	70"	8"	65"	80"	5"	72"	92"	3"	5'
41"	48"	18"	48"	57"	15"	55"	67"	12"	63"	77"	9"	71"	88"	6"	79"	101"	3"	5.5'
45"	53"	19"	52"	63"	16"	61"	73"	13"	69"	84"	9"	78"	97"	6"	87"	110"	3"	6'
48"	57"	21"	57"	68"	17"	66"	79"	14"	75"	91"	10"	84"	105"	7"	94"	119"	3"	6.5'
52"	61"	23"	61"	73"	19"	71"	85"	15"	80"	98"	11"	90"	113"	7"	101"	128"	4"	7'
56"	66"	24"	66"	78"	20"	76"	91"	16"	86"	105"	12"	97"	121"	8"	108"	137"	4"	7.5'
59"	70"	26"	70"	83"	21"	81"	97"	17"	92"	112"	13"	103"	129"	8"	115"	146"	4"	8'
63"	75"	27"	74"	89"	23"	86"	104"	18"	98"	120"	13"	110"	137"	9"	123"	156"	4"	8.5'
67"	79"	29"	79"	94"	24"	91"	110"	19"	103"	127"	14"	116"	145"	9"	130"	165"	5"	9'
71"	83"	31"	83"	99"	25"	96"	116"	20"	109"	134"	15"	123"	153"	10"	137"	174"	5"	9.5'
74"	88"	32"	87"	104"	27"	101"	122"	21"	115"	141"	16"	129"	161"	10"	144"	183"	5"	10'

Art Lighting for 30° Aiming Angle

Step 1: Find the fixture distance for the ceiling height. Figure 7.12

Step 2: Using the distance found in step 1, find the candlepower needed to provide the desired footcandle level (Fc). Figure 7.14

Note: The Fc level should be 5 times the ambient light level.

Step 3: Again using the distance found in step 1, find the width (W) of the beam ellipse that fits the width of the art. Then read up the column to find the beam angle. Figure 7.11

If the artwork is too wide, find a beam angle that will cover half the width and use two lamps, etc., until the width of the art is covered. Spacing (S) should be at least the ellipse width (W), allow some intersect if possible.

Step 4: Make sure that the length (L) of the ellipse will cover the height of the artwork and note the distance from the ceiling to the top of the ellipse (h). Figure 7.11

Note: The width (W) of the ellipse will always be centered on the point where nadir meets the wall, but the length (L) of the ellipse will not. Use (h) to locate the top of the ellipse from the ceiling to make sure the height of the artwork is properly illuminated.

Step 5: Go to Appendix A to locate a lamp with the candlepower found in step 2 and the beam angle found in step 3.

Footcandle Level

55Fc	60Fc	65Fc	70Fc	75Fc	80Fc	85Fc	90Fc	95Fc	100Fc	200Fc	Distance
85	92	100	108	115	123	131	139	146	154	308	1'
191	208	225	242	260	277	294	312	329	346	693	1.5'
339	370	400	431	462	493	523	554	585	616	1,232	2'
529	577	625	674	722	770	818	866	914	962	1,925	2.5'
762	831	901	970	1,039	1,109	1,178	1,247	1,316	1,386	2,771	3'
1,037	1,132	1,226	1,320	1,415	1,509	1,603	1,697	1,792	1,886	3,772	3.5'
1,355	1,478	1,601	1,724	1,848	1,971	2,094	2,217	2,340	2,463	4,927	4'
1,715	1,871	2,026	2,182	2,338	2,494	2,650	2,806	2,962	3,118	6,235	4.5'
2,117	2,309	2,502	2,694	2,887	3,079	3,272	3,464	3,657	3,849	7,698	5'
2,562	2,794	3,027	3,260	3,493	3,726	3,959	4,192	4,424	4,657	9,315	5.5'
3,048	3,326	3,603	3,880	4,157	4,434	4,711	4,988	5,265	5,543	11,085	6'
3,578	3,903	4,228	4,553	4,879	5,204	5,529	5,854	6,180	6,505	13,010	6.5'
4,149	4,526	4,904	5,281	5,658	6,035	6,412	6,790	7,167	7,544	15,088	7'
4,763	5,196	5,629	6,062	6,495	6,928	7,361	7,794	8,227	8,660	17,321	7.5'
5,419	5,912	6,405	6,897	7,390	7,883	8,375	8,868	9,361	9,853	19,707	8'
6,118	6,674	7,230	7,787	8,343	8,899	9,455	10,011	10,567	11,124	22,247	8.5'
6,859	7,482	8,106	8,730	9,353	9,977	10,600	11,224	11,847	12,471	24,942	9'
7,642	8,337	9,032	9,726	10,421	11,116	11,811	12,505	13,200	13,895	27,790	9.5'
8,468	9,238	10,007	10,777	11,547	12,317	13,087	13,856	14,626	15,396		10'

Δ ——— **Candlepower** ——— Δ

30° Aiming Angle

APPENDIX A

LAMP DATA

National Energy Policy Act (EPACT)

The National Energy Policy Act of 1992, which legislates the phased discontinuation of fluorescent and incandescent lamp types that don't meet specified LPW and CRI standards, offers lighting users the opportunity to take a fresh look at their lighting systems and select new cost-cutting options.

Designed to reduce national energy consumption dramatically, the legislation halted the manufacture of low-efficacy F96T12 and F96T12/HO lamps in Phase I (April 30, 1994) and affects general service F40 four-foot medium bi-pin , two-foot U-bent and incandescent PAR and reflector lamps in Phase III (October 31, 1995).

Phase II, the lamp labeling law, went into effect May 15, 1995 for fluorescent and

compact fluorescent lamp types and on December 1, 1995 for incandescent and halogen lamps. The law requires that the packaging for incandescent, halogen and compact fluorescent lamps prominently feature light output (lumens), energy used (watts) and rated life (hours) along with an advisory disclosure stating that, "To save energy cost, find the light output you need, then choose the lamp with the lowest watts." Fluorescent lamps and packaging must feature a Ⓔ, indicating that the lamp meets EPACT criteria.

Lamp manufacturers offer many energy-efficient lighting solutions that meet and surpass EPACT criteria and provide high quality light.

Courtesy *Phillips Lighting*

EPACT Upgrade Reference			
Obsolete Lamps	**GE**	**PHILIPS**	**OSRAM/SYLVANIA**
F40T12 CW F40T12 WW F40T12 D (40 Watt)	SPX Series F40T12 (34 Watt)	Ultralume F40T12 (34 Watt)	Designer 800 F40T12 (34 Watt)
R30	(1) SPX Series Compact Fluorescent (2) PAR30 Halogen	(1) Ultralume Compact Fluorescent (2) PAR30 Halogen	(1) Designer 800 Compact Fluorescent (2) PAR30 Capsylite
R40	(1) SPX Series Compact Fluorescent (2) PAR38 Halogen	(1) Ultralume Compact Fluorescent (2) PAR38 Halogen	(1) Designer 800 Compact Fluorescent (2) PAR38 Capsylite
PAR38	(1) SPX Series Compact Fluorescent (2) PAR38 Halogen	(1) Ultralume Compact Fluorescent (2) PAR38 Halogen	(1) Designer 800 Compact Fluorescent (2) PAR38 Capsylite
	(1) = Best Choice		(2) = Second Best Choice

Figure A.1   EPACT Upgrade Reference

The major lamp manufacturers provide a direct lamp conversion chart for their entire product offering which suggest good, better, best substitutions for lamps that have been discontinued according to EPACT. I have elected not to include them here because they can be somewhat misleading.

While some of the substitutions provide adequate lighting output, the beam angle can be quite different. R30 and R40 lamps have a much wider beam angle than most standard PAR floods for example. The substituted PAR lamp will not provide the same coverage as the R lamp.

It is my suggestion that you compare not only the light output, but also the beam angle for the most satisfactory substitution. The techniques in this book, along with the information contained in this Appendix, will help you do this. The EPACT Upgrade Reference on this page gives you a direction to pursue in finding an appropriate substitution for fluorescent and incandescent lamps.

Also consider replacing 8 foot fluorescent lamps with a pair of 4 footers. The ballast noise will be greatly reduced.

Base Types (Not Actual Sizes)

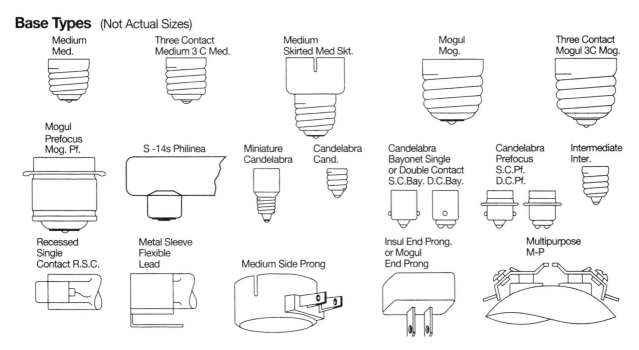

Bulb Shapes (Not Actual Sizes)

The size and shape of a bulb is designated by a letter or letters followed by a number. The letter indicates the shape of the bulb while the number indicates the diameter of the bulb in eighths of an inch. For example, "T-10" indicates a tubular shaped bulb having a diameter of $^{10}/_8$ or 1¼ inches. The following illustrations show some of the more popular bulb shapes and sizes.

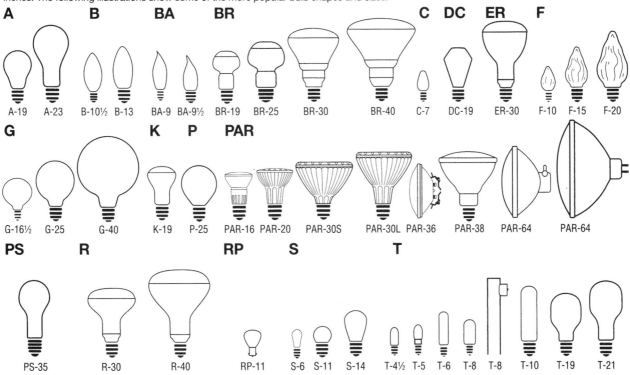

Figure A.2   Incandescent Lamp Bases and Shapes   *Courtesy Phillips*

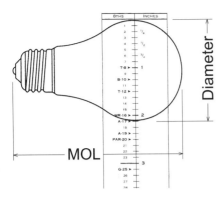

Figure A.3   ***Lamp Diameter & MOL***

Courtesy Sylvania/Osram

Lamp Diameter

One of the great mysteries of the lighting industry is the coding used to describe a lamp. There are A19, R30, R40, PAR16, PAR20, PAR30, PAR38, MR11, MR16, lamps to name a few. All of them are associated with a number. These numbers all mean something.

They indicate the width or diameter of the lamp measured in ***eighths*** of an inch. So a PAR30 is 30/8 or 3 3/4 inches in diameter. A MR16 is 16/8 or 2 inches in diameter, etc.

Regardless of how it is expressed, knowing the diameter of a lamp is useful when deciding upon a lamp for a fixture or trim, or when thinking about swapping one lamp for another, a PAR30 for a R30 for instance. They are both the same diameter and will probably fit similarly. However, not all lamps are the same length.

MOL (Maximum Overall Length)

From the crown of the lamp to the tip of its screw in, or plug in base is the MOL or Maximum Overall Length of the lamp. See

figure A.3. Be extra careful when using IC (Insulation Contact Housings) rated recessed cans. IC cans limit how far a lamp can be recessed into it and some lamps will actually protrude below the ceiling even though a manufacturer says they will work! They will if you don't care what they look like. For example, in some IC cans, an R30 will project a full inch below the ceiling while a PAR30 will be completely recessed with room to spare.

Appendix Conventions (Incandescent)

Incandescent - Some of the lamps listed are noted as discontinued as a result of EPACT but have been included for comparison purposes since these lamps will be available for sale until stocks are depleted.

EPACT Compliance

Ⓔ - Efficiency approved according to new Federal EPACT standards.

△ - Either exempt from EPACT, or EPACT guidelines do not apply (i.e., accent or task lighting).

Color Symbols

☺ - Means the lamp has a CRI of 80 or higher and a color temperature between 2,850k and 3,100k. See Chapter 2.

☺ - Means the lamp has a CRI over 70 and a color temperature between 2,850k and 3,200k. See Chapter 2.

Look for lamps with one of these two symbol pairs for best color and efficiency!

General Electric

Incandescent

Lamp Description	Part Number	Volts	Lumens	L/W	Hours	MOL	Color Temp	CRI	Candle Power	Beam Angle
R20										
Incandescent										
									45 Watt	
45R20/MI	17808	120	440	10	2,000	3 1/4"	2,700k	100	530	43°
									50 Watt	
50R20	16693	120	410	8	2,000	3 1/4"	2,700k	100	510	45°
Incandescent Discontinued - for comparison only										
									30 Watt	
30W/R20	*		200	7	2,000		2,700k	100	220	43°
									50 Watt	
50W/R20	*		410	8	2,000		2,700k	100	510	43°
R30										
Incandescent Discontinued - for comparison only										
									50 Watt	
50W/R30/FL	*		525	11	2,000		2,700k	100	300	66°
									75 Watt	
75W/R30/FL	*		900	12	2,000		2,700k	100	470	72°
75W/R30/SP	*		900	12	2,000		2,700k	100	1,350	30°
BR30										
Incandescent										
									45 Watt	
45R/FL/MI	20330	120	485	11	2,000	5 3/8"	2,700k	100	300	66°
									60 Watt	
60R30/FL/K	11861	120	775	13	2,000	5 3/8"	2,700k	100	510	65°
60R30/SP/K	11862	120	775	13	2,000	5 3/8"	2,700k	100	1,600	30°
									65 Watt	
75R30/FL/65WM	15709	120	770	12	2,000	5 3/8"	2,700k	100	510	64°
75R30/SP/65WM	15711	120	770	12	2,000	5 3/8"	2,700k	100	1,600	30°
R40										
Incandescent Discontinued - for comparison only										
									100 Watt	
100W/R40/FL	*		1,190	12	2,000		2,700k	100	770	64°
100W/R40/SP	*		1,190	12	2,000		2,700k	100	3,000	24°
									150 Watt	
150W/R40/FL	*		1,900	13	2,000		2,700k	100	1,400	59°
150W/R40/SP	*		1,900	13	2,000		2,700k	100	4,600	25°
BR40										
Incandescent										
									65 Watt	
75R40/FL/65WM	14265	120	730	11	2,000	5 3/8"	2,700k	100	590	55°
									90 Watt	
100R40/FL/90WM	14267	120	1,100	12	2,000	6 1/2"	2,700k	100	900	55°

Phillips

Incandescent

Lamp Description	Part Number	Volts	Lumens	L/W	Hours	MOL	Color Temp	CRI	Candle Power	Beam Angle
R20										
Incandescent Discontinued - for comparison only										
									30 Watt	
30W/R20	*		200	7	2,000		2,700k	100	220	43°
									50 Watt	
50W/R20	*		410	8	2,000		2,700k	100	510	43°
R30										
Incandescent Discontinued - for comparison only										
									50 Watt	
50W/R30/FL	*		525	11	2,000		2,700k	100	300	66°
									75 Watt	
75W/R30/FL	*		900	12	2,000		2,700k	100	470	72°
75W/R30/SP	*		900	12	2,000		2,700k	100	1,350	30°
BR30										
Incandescent										
									65 Watt	
65BR30/FL55	22519-3	120	685	11	2,000	5 3/8"	2,700k	100	525	55°
65BR30/SP20	22522-7	120	685	11	2,000	5 3/8"	2,700k	100	1,625	20°
									85 Watt	
85BR30/FL55	22517-7	120	925	11	2,000	5 3/8"	2,700k	100	700	55°
85BR30/SP20	22700-9	120	925	11	2,000	5 3/8"	2,700k	100	3,100	20°
R40										
Incandescent Discontinued - for comparison only										
									100 Watt	
100W/R40/FL	*		1,190	12	2,000		2,700k	100	770	64°
100W/R40/SP	*		1,190	12	2,000		2,700k	100	3,000	24°
									150 Watt	
150W/R40/FL	*		1,900	13	2,000		2,700k	100	1,400	59°
150W/R40/SP	*		1,900	13	2,000		2,700k	100	4,600	25°
BR40										
Incandescent										
									65 Watt	
65BR40/FL60	22536-7	120	685	11	2,000	6 1/2"	2,700k	100	500	60°
									85 Watt	
85BR40/FL60	22542-5	120	925	11	2,000	6 1/2"	2,700k	100	700	60°
85BR40/SP20	22694-4	120	925	11	2,000	6 1/2"	2,700k	100	3,100	20°

Sylvania-Osram   Incandescent

	Lamp Description	Part Number	Volts	Lumens	L/W	Hours	MOL	Color Temp	CRI	Candle Power	Beam Angle
R20											
	Incandescent										
										30 Watt	
	30R20	14794	120		n/a	2,000	3 3/4"	2,700k	100	300	40°
										50 Watt	
	50R20/RP	14833	120		n/a	2,000	3 3/4"	2,700k	100	550	45°
	Incandescent Discontinued - for comparison only										
										30 Watt	
	30W/R20	*		200	7	2,000		2,700k	100	220	43°
										50 Watt	
	50W/R20	*		410	8	2,000		2,700k	100	510	43°
R30											
	Incandescent Discontinued - for comparison only										
										50 Watt	
	50W/R30/FL	*		525	11	2,000		2,700k	100	300	66°
										75 Watt	
	75W/R30/FL	*		900	12	2,000		2,700k	100	470	72°
	75W/R30/SP	*		900	12	2,000		2,700k	100	1,350	30°
BR30											
	Incandescent										
										65 Watt	
Ⓔ	65BR30/FL/ES	15024	120	715	11	2,000	5 3/8"	2,700k	100	380	140°
Ⓔ	65BR30/SP/ES	15027	120	715	11	2,000	5 3/8"	2,700k	100	1,600	30°
										75 Watt	
Ⓔ	75BR30/FL/RP	15121	120	938	13	2,000	5 3/8"	2,700k	100	470	140°
	75BR30/SP/RP	15122	120	770	10	2,000	5 3/8"	2,700k	100	1,600	30°
R40											
	Incandescent Discontinued - for comparison only										
										100 Watt	
	100W/R40/FL	*		1,190	12	2,000		2,700k	100	770	64°
	100W/R40/SP	*		1,190	12	2,000		2,700k	100	3,000	24°
										150 Watt	
	150W/R40/FL	*		1,900	13	2,000		2,700k	100	1,400	59°
	150W/R40/SP	*		1,900	13	2,000		2,700k	100	4,600	25°
BR40											
	Incandescent										
										75 Watt	
	75BR/FL/RP	15128	120	770	10	2,000	6 1/2"	2,700k	100	460	140°
										100 Watt	
	100BR/FL	14851	120	935	9	2,000	6 1/2"	2,700k	100	900	120°

General Electric

Halogen

Lamp Description	Part Number	Volts	Lumens	L/W	Hours	MOL	Color Temp	CRI	Candle Power	Beam Angle
TB-19										
Halogen Performance Plus A-Line										
									50	**Watt**
50TB/H	16746	120	710	14	2,000	4 1/2"	2,800k	100		
									90	**Watt**
☺ 90TB/H	16744	120	1,580	18	2,000	4 1/2"	2,930k	100		
PAR20										
Halogen Performance Plus										
									50	**Watt**
50PAR20/H/NFL25°	17867	120	570	11	2,000	3 1/8"	2,800k	100	1,500	27°
50PAR20/FL/HAL	14928	120	570	11	2,000	3 1/8"	2,800k	100	1,850	27°
50PAR20/SP/HAL	14927	120	570	11	2,000	3 1/8"	2,800k	100	6,000	10°
50PAR20/H/NSP8°	17864	120	570	11	2,000	3 1/8"	2,800k	100	6,000	8°
PAR30										
Halogen IR										
									50	**Watt**
Ⓔ 50PAR30/HIR/FL35°	19900	120	770	15	3,000	3 5/8"	2,810k	100	1,600	37°
Ⓔ 50PAR30/HIR/NFL25°	19901	120	770	15	3,000	3 5/8"	2,810k	100	3,000	25°
Ⓔ 50PAR30/HIR/NSP8°	19902	120	770	15	3,000	3 5/8"	2,810k	100	17,000	8°
Halogen Performance Plus										
									75	**Watt**
Ⓔ 75PAR30/H/FL35°	18059	120	1,030	14	2,000	3 5/8"	2,830k	100	2,000	37°
Ⓔ 75PAR30/H/NFL25°	18057	120	1,030	14	2,000	3 5/8"	2,830k	100	3,100	27°
Ⓔ 75PAR30/H/NSP9°	18055	120	1,030	14	2,000	3 5/8"	2,830k	100	13,000	9°

General Electric

Halogen

		Lamp Description	Part Number	Volts	Lumens	L/W	Hours	MOL	Color Temp	CRI	Candle Power	Beam Angle
PAR38												
		Halogen Common										
											50	**Watt**
Ⓔ		50PAR38/H/FL	17925	120	590	12	2,000		2,750k	100	2,200	25°
Ⓔ		50PAR38/H/SP	17927	120	590	12	2,000		2,750k	100	9,000	10°
											100	**Watt**
Ⓔ	☺	100PAR38/H/FL	17946	120	1,400	14	2,000	5 3/8"	2,900k	100	4,800	27°
Ⓔ	☺	100PAR38/H/SP	17951	120	1,400	14	2,000	5 3/8"	2,900k	100	17,000	11°
		Halogen IR										
											50	**Watt**
Ⓔ		50PAR38/HIR/25°	12397	120	850	17	3,000	5 3/8"	2,810k	100	3,000	27°
Ⓔ		50PAR38/HIR/9°	12936	120	850	17	3,000	5 3/8"	2,810k	100	14,000	9°
											60	**Watt**
Ⓔ	☺	60PAR38/HIR/WFL	20947	120	1,110	19	3,000	5 3/8"	2,875k	100	1,250	53°
Ⓔ	☺	60PAR38/HIR/40°	10467	120	1,110	19	3,000	5 3/8"	2,875k	100	2,000	40°
Ⓔ	☺	60PAR38/HIR/FL30°	18626	120	1,110	19	3,000	5 3/8"	2,875k	100	3,600	28°
Ⓔ	☺	60PAR38/HIR/SP10°	18627	120	1,110	19	3,000	5 3/8"	2,875k	100	16,000	10°
											100	**Watt**
Ⓔ	☺	100PAR38/HIR/40°	10473	120	2,070	21	3,000	5 3/8"	2,900k	100	3,400	40°
Ⓔ	☺	100PAR38/HIR/NFL25°	18631	120	2,070	21	3,000	5 3/8"	2,900k	100	7,500	27°
Ⓔ	☺	100PAR38/HIR/SP10°	18635	120	2,070	21	3,000	5 3/8"	2,900k	100	29,000	10°
		Halogen Performance Plus										
											45	**Watt**
Ⓔ		45PAR38/H/FL25°	16230	120	510	11	2,500	5 3/8"	2,750k	100	1,800	27°
Ⓔ		45PAR38/H/SP11°	16228	120	510	11	2,500	5 3/8"	2,750k	100	7,000	11°
											75	**Watt**
Ⓔ	☺	75PAR38/H/NFL25°	21387	120	1,030	14	2,500	5 3/8"	2,850k	100	4,000	25°
Ⓔ	☺	75PAR38/H/NSP9°	21388	120	1,030	14	2,500	5 3/8"	2,850k	100	18,000	9°
											90	**Watt**
Ⓔ	☺	90PAR38/H/FL25°	13307	120	1,260	14	2,500	5 3/8"	2,870k	100	4,100	27°
Ⓔ	☺	90PAR38/H/SP10°	13309	120	1,260	14	2,500	5 3/8"	2,870k	100	16,000	10°
		Halogen Performance Plus Cool Beam										
											90	**Watt**
Ⓔ	☺	90PAR38/CB/H/FL25°	17691	120	1,260	14	2,500	5 3/8"	2,870k	100	4,100	27°

Phillips   Halogen

Lamp Description	Part Number	Volts	Lumens	L/W	Hours	MOL	Color Temp	CRI	Candle Power	Beam Angle
PAR16										
Halogen MasterLine										
40 Watt										
☺ 40PAR16/HAL/NFL27	33001-9	120	400	10	2,000	3 1/5"	3,000k	100	1,300	27°
☺ 40PAR16/HAL/NSP10	32999-5	120	400	10	2,000	3 1/5"	3,000k	100	5,000	10°
60 Watt										
☺ 60PAR16/HAL/NFL27	33006-8	120	580	10	2,000	3 1/5"	3,000k	100	2,000	27°
☺ 60PAR16/HAL/NSP10	33004-3	120	580	10	2,000	3 1/5"	3,000k	100	7,500	10°
PAR20										
Halogen MasterLine WISO Reflector										
50 Watt										
☺ 50PAR20/HAL/NFL30	22911-2	120	550	11	2,000	3 3/8"	3,000k	100	1,400	30°
☺ 50PAR20/HAL/SP16	22908-8	120	550	11	2,000	3 3/8"	3,000k	100	3,200	16°
☺ 50PAR20/HAL/NSP9	22906-2	120	550	11	2,000	3 3/8"	3,000k	100	6,200	9°
PAR30										
Halogen MasterLine WISO Reflector										
60 Watt										
Ⓔ ☺ 60PAR30S/HAL/FL40	35758-2	120	800	13	2,500	3 5/8"	3,000k	100	1,850	40°
Ⓔ ☺ 60PAR30S/HAL/NFL30	35753-3	120	800	13	2,500	3 5/8"	3,000k	100	3,300	30°
Ⓔ ☺ 60PAR30S/HAL/NSP10	35751-7	120	800	13	2,500	3 5/8"	3,000k	100	10,000	10°
PAR38										
Halogen MasterLine										
45 Watt										
Ⓔ ☺ 45PAR38/HAL/FL28	22948-4	120	530	12	2,500	5 1/4"	3,000k	100	2,000	28°
Ⓔ ☺ 45PAR38/HAL/SP12	22946-8	120	530	12	2,500	5 1/4"	3,000k	100	5,800	12°
60 Watt										
Ⓔ ☺ 60PAR38/HAL/FL28	23065-6	120	880	15	2,500	5 1/4"	3,000k	100	3,500	28°
Ⓔ ☺ 60PAR38/HAL/SP12	23062-3	120	880	15	2,500	5 1/4"	3,000k	100	13,500	12°
Ⓔ ☺ 60PAR38/HAL/NSP9	23059-9	120	880	15	2,500	5 1/4"	3,000k	100	15,500	9°
75 Watt										
Ⓔ ☺ 75PAR38/HAL/FL27	23067-2	120	1,050	14	2,500	5 1/4"	3,000k	100	4,500	27°
Ⓔ ☺ 75PAR38/HAL/SP10	23066-4	120	1,050	14	2,500	5 1/4"	3,000k	100	14,500	10°
90 Watt										
Ⓔ ☺ 90PAR38/HAL/FL28	23070-6	120	1,280	14	2,500	5 1/4"	3,000k	100	4,500	28°
Ⓔ ☺ 90PAR38/HAL/SP12	23069-8	120	1,280	14	2,500	5 1/4"	3,000k	100	14,500	12°
Halogen MasterLine WISO Reflector										
90 Watt										
Ⓔ ☺ 90PAR38/HAL/WFL60	23646-3	120	1,400	16	2,500	5 1/4"	3,000k	100	1,300	60°

Sylvania-Osram

Halogen

Lamp Description	Part Number	Volts	Lumens	L/W	Hours	MOL	Color Temp	CRI	Candle Power	Beam Angle
MB-19										
Halogen Capsylite A-Line										
									42 Watt	
☺ 42MB/CAP	18907	120	570	14	3,500	4 3/8"	3,000k	100		
									52 Watt	
☺ 52MB/CAP	18921	120	770	15	3,500	4 3/8"	3,000k	100		
									60 Watt	
☺ 60A/HAL	18960	120	960	16	3,000	4 3/8"	3,000k	100		
									72 Watt	
☺ 72MB/CAP	18937	120	1,150	16	3,500	4 3/8"	3,000k	100		
									75 Watt	
☺ 75A/HAL	18965	120	1,300	17	2,250	4 3/8"	3,000k	100		
									100 Watt	
☺ 100A/HAL	18970	120	1,850	19	2,250	4 3/8"	3,000k	100		
PAR16										
Halogen Capsylite										
									60 Watt	
☺ 60PAR16/CAP/NFL/30	59030	120		n/a	2,000	2 7/8"	3,000k	100	1,300	30°
☺ 60PAR16/CAP/NSP/10	59032	120		n/a	2,000	2 7/8"	3,000k	100	5,000	10°
									75 Watt	
☺ 75PAR16/CAP/NFL/30	59034	120		n/a	2,000	2 7/8"	3,000k	100	1,900	30°
☺ 75PAR16/CAP/NSP/10	59036	120		n/a	2,000	2 7/8"	3,000k	100	7,500	10°
PAR20										
Halogen Capsylite										
									35 Watt	
☺ 35PAR20/CAP/WFL/40	14506	120		n/a	2,500	3 1/4"	3,000k	100	600	40°
☺ 35PAR20/CAP/NFL/30	14464	120		n/a	2,500	3 1/4"	3,000k	100	900	30°
☺ 35PAR20/CAP/NSP/8	14467	120		n/a	2,500	3 1/4"	3,000k	100	3,000	8°
									50 Watt	
☺ 50PAR20/CAP/NFL/30	14525	120		n/a	2,500	3 1/4"	3,000k	100	1,250	30°
☺ 50PAR20/CAP/NSP/10	14524	120		n/a	2,500	3 1/4"	3,000k	100	5,000	10°
PAR30										
Halogen Capsylite										
									50 Watt	
Ⓔ ☺ 50PAR30/CAP/FL/40	14532	120	600	12	2,500	3 5/8"	3,000k	100	1,300	40°
Ⓔ ☺ 50PAR30/CAP/NFL/30	14527	120	600	12	2,500	3 5/8"	3,000k	100	1,850	30°
Ⓔ ☺ 50PAR30/CAP/NSP/9	14526	120	600	12	2,500	3 5/8"	3,000k	100	8,000	9°
									75 Watt	
Ⓔ ☺ 75PAR30/CAP/FL/40	14606	120	1,100	15	2,500	3 5/8"	3,000k	100	2,000	40°
Ⓔ ☺ 75PAR30/CAP/NFL/30	14603	120	1,100	15	2,500	3 5/8"	3,000k	100	3,200	30°
Ⓔ ☺ 75PAR30/CAP/NSP/9	14604	120	1,100	15	2,500	3 5/8"	3,000k	100	14,000	9°

Sylvania-Osram

Halogen

PAR38

Halogen Capsylite

		Lamp Description	Part Number	Volts	Lumens	L/W	Hours	MOL	Color Temp	CRI	Candle Power	Beam Angle
									45	**Watt**		
Ⓔ	☺	45PAR38/CAP/WFL/50	14010	120	520	12	2,500	5 1/4"	3,000k	100	600	50°
Ⓔ	☺	45PAR38/CAP/FL/30	14588	120	520	12	2,500	5 1/4"	3,000k	100	1,700	30°
Ⓔ	☺	45PAR38/CAP/SP/12	14589	120	520	12	2,500	5 1/4"	3,000k	100	5,500	12°
Ⓔ	☺	45PAR38/CAP/NSP/9	14590	120	520	12	2,500	5 1/4"	3,000k	100	10,000	9°
									60	**Watt**		
Ⓔ	☺	60PAR38/CAP/FL/30	14468	120	900	15	2,500	5 1/4"	3,000k	100	3,200	30°
Ⓔ	☺	60PAR38/CAP/WSP/12	14423	120	900	15	2,500	5 1/4"	3,000k	100	10,000	12°
Ⓔ	☺	60PAR38/CAP/SP/10	14469	120	900	15	2,500	5 1/4"	3,000k	100	17,500	10°
									75	**Watt**		
Ⓔ	☺	75PAR38/CAP/FL/30	14513	120	1,040	14	2,500	5 1/4"	3,000k	100	3,300	30°
Ⓔ	☺	75PAR38/CAP/WSP/12	14510	120	1,040	14	2,500	5 1/4"	3,000k	100	11,000	12°
Ⓔ	☺	75PAR38/CAP/SP/10	14514	120	1,040	14	2,500	5 1/4"	3,000k	100	17,500	10°
									90	**Watt**		
Ⓔ	☺	90PAR38/CAP/WFL/50	14602	130	1,300	14	2,500	5 1/4"	3,000k	100	1,500	50°
Ⓔ	☺	90PAR38/CAP/FL/30	14579	120	1,300	14	2,500	5 1/4"	3,000k	100	3,750	30°
Ⓔ	☺	90PAR38/CAP/SP/12	14580	120	1,300	14	2,500	5 1/4"	3,000k	100	12,000	12°
Ⓔ	☺	90PAR38/CAP/NSP/9	14586	120	1,300	14	2,500	5 1/4"	3,000k	100	19,500	9°

Halogen Capsylite Coated Cool Lux

		Lamp Description	Part Number	Volts	Lumens	L/W	Hours	MOL	Color Temp	CRI	Candle Power	Beam Angle
									90	**Watt**		
Ⓔ	☺	90PAR38/CAP/2FL/30	14971	120	1,260	14	2,500	5 1/4"	3,000k	100	3,750	30°
Ⓔ	☺	90PAR38/CAP/2SP12	14972	120	1,260	14	2,500	5 1/4"	3,000k	100	11,000	12°

General Electric

Halogen Low Voltage

		Lamp Description	Part Number	Volts	Lumens	L/W	Hours	MOL	Color Temp	CRI	Candle Power	Beam Angle
MR11												
		Halogen Low Voltage Precise										
											20	**Watt**
△	☺	Q20MR11/NFL30°	(FTD)	30773	12		n/a	3,500	1 3/8"	2,900k	100	600	30°
											35	**Watt**
△	☺	Q35MR11/NFL30°	(FTH)	30890	12		n/a	3,500	1 3/8"	2,900k	100	1,300	30°
△	☺	Q35MR11/SP20°	(FTF)	30774	12		n/a	3,500	1 3/8"	2,900k	100	3,000	20°
MR16												
		Halogen Low Voltage Precise										
											20	**Watt**
△	☺	Q20MR16/FL40°	(BAB)	14790	12		n/a	4,000	1 7/8"	2,900k	100	525	40°
△	☺	Q20MR16/NSP15°	(ESX)	14789	12		n/a	4,000	1 7/8"	2,900k	100	3,600	13°
											35	**Watt**
△	☺	Q35MR16/FL40°	(FMW)	19984	12		n/a	4,000	1 7/8"	3,000k	100	1,000	40°
△	☺	Q35MR16/SP20°	(FRA)	19983	12		n/a	4,000	1 7/8"	3,000k	100	3,900	20°
											42	**Watt**
△	☺	Q42MR16/NFL25°	(EYS)	14785	12		n/a	4,000	1 7/8"	3,000k	100	2,400	27°
△	☺	Q42MR16/VNSP9°	(EZY)	14945	12		n/a	3,500	1 7/8"	3,000k	100	13,100	9°
											50	**Watt**
△	☺	Q50MR16/WFL55°	(FNV)	18710	12		n/a	4,000	1 7/8"	3,050k	100	1,000	55°
△	☺	Q50MR16/FL40°	(EXN)	14788	12		n/a	4,000	1 7/8"	3,050k	100	1,850	40°
△	☺	Q50MR16/FL/1	(ENL)	39857	12		n/a	4,000	1 7/8"	3,050k	100	2,325	32°
△	☺	Q50MR16/NFL25°	(EXZ)	14793	12		n/a	4,000	1 7/8"	3,050k	100	3,400	27°
△	☺	Q50MR16/NSP15°	(EXT)	14787	12		n/a	4,000	1 7/8"	3,050k	100	10,200	14°
											71	**Watt**
△	☺	Q71MR16/FL40°	(EYC)	14794	12		n/a	4,000	1 7/8"	3,050k	100	2,100	42°
△	☺	Q71MR16/NFL25°	(EYJ)	15941	12		n/a	4,000	1 7/8"	3,050k	100	4,900	27°
△	☺	Q71MR16/NSP15°	(EYF)	14795	12		n/a	4,000	1 7/8"	3,050k	100	12,000	14°
		Halogen Low Voltage Precise ConstantColor										
											20	**Watt**
△	☺	Q20MR16/C/FL40°	(BAB)	20814	12		n/a	5,000	1 7/8"	2,900k	100	525	40°
△	☺	Q20MR16/C/NSP15°	(ESX)	20815	12		n/a	5,000	1 7/8"	2,900k	100	3,600	13°
△	☺	Q20MR16/C/VNSP7°	(EZX)	20816	12		n/a	3,000	1 7/8"	2,900k	100	7,400	7°
											35	**Watt**
△	☺	Q35MR16/C/FL40°	(FMW)	20825	12		n/a	4,000	1 7/8"	3,000k	100	1,000	40°
△	☺	Q35MR16/C/SP20°	(FRA)	20826	12		n/a	4,000	1 7/8"	3,000k	100	3,900	20°
											42	**Watt**
△	☺	Q42MR16/C/NFL25°	(EYS)	20828	12		n/a	5,000	1 7/8"	3,000k	100	1,900	24°
△	☺	Q42MR16/C/VNSP9°	(EZY)	20830	12		n/a	3,500	1 7/8"	3,000k	100	13,100	9°
											50	**Watt**
△	☺	Q50MR16/C/WFL55°	(FNV)	20832	12		n/a	5,000	1 7/8"	3,050k	100	900	55°
△	☺	Q50MR16/C/FL40°	(EXN)	20833	12		n/a	5,000	1 7/8"	3,050k	100	1,850	40°
△	☺	Q50MR16/C/NFL30°	(EXK)	20834	12		n/a	5,000	1 7/8"	3,050k	100	2,450	32°
△	☺	Q50MR16/C/NFL25°	(EXZ)	20835	12		n/a	5,000	1 7/8"	3,050k	100	3,400	27°
△	☺	Q50MR16/C/VNSP15°	(EXT)	20839	12		n/a	5,000	1 7/8"	3,050k	100	10,200	14°
											71	**Watt**
△	☺	Q71MR16/C/FL40°	(EYC)	20840	12		n/a	4,000	1 7/8"	3,050k	100	2,100	42°

General Electric

Halogen Low Voltage

		Lamp Description		Part Number	Volts	Lumens	L/W	Hours	MOL	Color Temp	CRI	Candle Power	Beam Angle
△	☺	Q71MR16/C/NFL25°	(EYJ)	20841	12		n/a	4,000	1 7/8"	3,050k	100	4,900	25°
△	☺	Q71MR16/C/NSP15°	(EYF)	20843	12		n/a	4,000	1 7/8"	3,050k	100	12,000	14°

Halogen Low Voltage Precise ConstantColor Cover Glass

		Lamp Description		Part Number	Volts	Lumens	L/W	Hours	MOL	Color Temp	CRI	Candle Power	Beam Angle
												20	***Watt***
△	☺	Q20MR16/C/CG40°	(BAB)	20857	12		n/a	5,000	1 7/8"	2,900k	100	490	40°
△	☺	Q20MR16/C/CG15°	(ESX)	20858	12		n/a	5,000	1 7/8"	2,900k	100	3,350	13°
												35	***Watt***
△	☺	Q35MR16/C/CG40°	(FMW)	20859	12		n/a	4,000	1 7/8"	3,000k	100	900	40°
△	☺	Q35MR16/C/CG20°	(FRA)	20860	12		n/a	4,000	1 7/8"	3,000k	100	3,625	20°
												50	***Watt***
△	☺	Q50MR16/C/CG55°	(FNV)	20865	12		n/a	5,000	1 7/8"	3,050k	100	850	55°
△	☺	Q50MR16/C/CG40°	(EXN)	20867	12		n/a	5,000	1 7/8"	3,050k	100	1,720	40°
△	☺	Q50MR16/C/CG25°	(EXZ)	20871	12		n/a	5,000	1 7/8"	3,050k	100	3,160	27°
△	☺	Q50MR16/C/CG15°	(EXT)	20872	12		n/a	5,000	1 7/8"	3,050k	100	9,500	14°
												71	***Watt***
△	☺	Q71MR16/C/CG40°	(EYC)	20873	12		n/a	4,000	1 7/8"	3,050k	100	1,950	42°
△	☺	Q71MR16/C/CG25°	(EYJ)	20874	12		n/a	4,000	1 7/8"	3,050k	100	4,560	25°
△	☺	Q71MR16/C/CG15°	(EYF)	20876	12		n/a	4,000	1 7/8"	3,050k	100	11,200	12°

Phillips

Halogen Low Voltage

		Lamp Description		Part Number	Volts	Lumens	L/W	Hours	MOL	Color Temp	CRI	Candle Power	Beam Angle
MR11													
		Halogen Low Voltage Closed Cover Glass											
												20 Watt	
△	☺	20MRC11/FL30		30109-3	12		n/a	2,000	1 5/8"	2,925k	100	600	30°
△	☺	20MRC11/SP10		30104-4	12		n/a	2,000	1 5/8"	2,925k	100	5,500	10°
MR16													
		Halogen Low Voltage Accent 1200											
												20 Watt	
△	☺	20MR16/FL36	(BAB)	37495-9	12		n/a	3,500	1 3/4"	2,925k	100	550	36°
△	☺	20MR16/SP10	(ESX)	37487-6	12		n/a	3,500	1 3/4"	2,925k	100	4,200	10°
												50 Watt	
△	☺	50MR16/FL38	(EXN)	37498-3	12		n/a	4,000	1 3/4"	3,050k	100	1,800	38°
△	☺	50MR16/NFL24	(EXZ)	37497-5	12		n/a	4,000	1 3/4"	3,050k	100	3,200	24°
△	☺	50MR16/SP10	(EXT)	37496-7	12		n/a	4,000	1 3/4"	3,050k	100	11,000	10°
												75 Watt	
△	☺	75MR16/FL36	(EYC)	37500-6	12		n/a	4,000	1 3/4"	3,050k	100	2,500	36°
△	☺	75MR16/SP14	(EYF)	37499-1	12		n/a	4,000	1 3/4"	3,050k	100	12,800	14°
		Halogen Low Voltage Closed Cover Glass											
												20 Watt	
△	☺	20MRC16/FL36		33304-7	12		n/a	2,000	1 7/8"	2,925k	100	650	36°
△	☺	20MRC16/SP10		33303-9	12		n/a	2,000	1 7/8"	2,925k	100	4,100	10°
												50 Watt	
△	☺	50MRC16/FL36		33307-0	12		n/a	3,000	1 7/8"	3,050k	100	1,800	36°
△	☺	50MRC16/NFL24		33306-2	12		n/a	3,000	1 7/8"	3,050k	100	3,100	24°
△	☺	50MRC16/SP10		33305-4	12		n/a	3,000	1 7/8"	3,050k	100	10,000	10°
		Halogen Low Voltage Closed Cover Glass Aluminum											
												50 Watt	
△	☺	50MRC16/FL40/A		35639-4	12		n/a	4,000	1 7/8"	3,000k	100	1,500	40°
△	☺	50MRC16/NFL24/A		35640-2	12		n/a	4,000	1 7/8"	3,000k	100	3,200	24°
△	☺	50MRC16/SP12/A		35638-6	12		n/a	4,000	1 7/8"	3,000k	100	9,000	12°
ALR													
		Halogen Low Voltage Closed Aluminum Reflector (ALR)											
												15 Watt	
△	☺	15ALR18/SP14	(GBC)	32839-3	6		n/a	2,000	2 1/5"	3,000k	100	1,400	14°
												20 Watt	
△	☺	20ALR12/FL32	(GBF)	34003-4	12		n/a	2,000	1 3/8"	3,000k	100	350	32°
△	☺	20ALR12/SP18	(GBE)	34002-6	12		n/a	2,000	1 3/8"	3,000k	100	1,400	18°
△	☺	20ALR12/NSP6	(GBD)	32840-1	12		n/a	2,000	1 3/8"	3,000k	100	7,000	6°
												50 Watt	
△	☺	50ALR18/NFL25	(GBK)	34091-9	12		n/a	2,000	2 1/5"	3,000k	100	1,900	25°
△	☺	50ALR18/SP10	(GBJ)	32826-0	12		n/a	2,000	2 1/5"	3,000k	100	11,000	10°

Sylvania-Osram

Halogen Low Voltage

Lamp Description	Part Number	Volts	Lumens	L/W	Hours	MOL	Color Temp	CRI	Candle Power	Beam Angle
MR11										
Halogen Low Voltage Tru-Aim										
									20	**Watt**
△ ☺ 20MR11Q/40°/FL (FTD)	55107	12		n/a	2,000		3,000k	100	680	40°
△ ☺ 20MR11Q/25°/MFL (FTC)	55108	12		n/a	2,000		3,000k	100	1,450	25°
△ ☺ 20MR11Q/10°/SP (FTB)	55109	12		n/a	2,000		3,000k	100	5,000	10°
									35	**Watt**
△ ☺ 35MR11Q/40°/FL (FTH)	55111	12		n/a	3,000		3,000k	100	1,100	40°
△ ☺ 35MR11Q/25°/MFL (FTF)	55112	12		n/a	3,000		3,000k	100	2,400	25°
△ ☺ 35MR11Q/10°/SP (FTE)	55113	12		n/a	3,000		3,000k	100	6,500	10°
									50	**Watt**
△ ☺ 50MR11Q/40°/FL	55115	12		n/a	3,000		3,000k	100	1,600	40°
△ ☺ 50MR11Q/25°/MFL	55116	12		n/a	3,000		3,000k	100	3,400	25°
△ ☺ 50MR11Q/10°/SP	55117	12		n/a	3,000		3,000k	100	8,000	10°
MR16										
Halogen Low Voltage Tru-Aim										
									20	**Watt**
△ ☺ 20MR16Q/40°/FL (BAB)	58600	12		n/a	2,000		3,000k	100	700	40°
△ ☺ 20MR16Q/8°/NSP (ESX)	58601	12		n/a	2,000		3,000k	100	5,000	8°
									35	**Watt**
△ ☺ 35MR16Q/35°/FL (FMW)	58603	12		n/a	3,000		3,000k	100	1,400	35°
△ ☺ 35MR16Q/8°/NSP (FRB)	58604	12		n/a	3,000		3,000k	100	11,000	8°
									50	**Watt**
△ ☺ 50MR16Q/40°/FL (EXN)	58607	12		n/a	3,500		3,000k	100	2,000	40°
△ ☺ 50MR16Q/25°/NFL (EXZ)	58605	12		n/a	3,500		3,000k	100	3,200	25°
△ ☺ 50MR16Q/12°/NSP (EXT)	58608	12		n/a	3,500		3,000k	100	11,000	12°
									65	**Watt**
△ ☺ 65MR16Q/40°/FL (FPB)	58564	12		n/a	3,500		3,000k	100	2,100	40°
△ ☺ 65MR16Q/25°/NFL (FPC)	58565	12		n/a	3,500		3,000k	100	4,000	25°
△ ☺ 65MR16Q/10°/NSP (FPA)	58563	12		n/a	3,500		3,000k	100	14,000	10°
									75	**Watt**
△ ☺ 75MR16Q/40°/FL (EYC)	58627	12		n/a	3,500		3,000k	100	2,100	40°
△ ☺ 75MR16Q/25°/NFL (EYJ)	58610	12		n/a	3,500		3,000k	100	4,000	25°
△ ☺ 75MR16Q/13°/NSP (EYF)	58628	12		n/a	3,500		3,000k	100	12,500	13°
Halogen Low Voltage Tru-Aim Brilliant										
									20	**Watt**
△ ☺ 20MR16Q/35°/FL/B	58590	12		n/a	2,000		3,000k	100	625	35°
△ ☺ 20MR16Q/8°/NSP/B	58589	12		n/a	2,000		3,000k	100	4,650	8°
									35	**Watt**
△ ☺ 35MR16Q/35°/FL/B	58593	12		n/a	3,000		3,000k	100	1,300	35°
△ ☺ 35MR16Q/10°/NSP/B	58591	12		n/a	3,000		3,000k	100	8,700	10°
									50	**Watt**
△ ☺ 50MR16Q/35°/FL/B	58596	12		n/a	3,500		3,000k	100	1,900	35°
△ ☺ 50MR16Q/25°/NFL/B	58595	12		n/a	3,500		3,000k	100	3,000	25°
△ ☺ 50MR16Q/11°/NSP/B	58594	12		n/a	3,500		3,000k	100	10,500	11°
									65	**Watt**
△ ☺ 65MR16Q/35°/FL/B	58560	12		n/a	3,500		3,000k	100	2,100	35°

Sylvania-Osram

Halogen Low Voltage

		Lamp Description	Part Number	Volts	Lumens	L/W	Hours	MOL	Color Temp	CRI	Candle Power	Beam Angle
△	☺	65MR16Q/25°/NFL/B	58561	12		n/a	3,500		3,000k	100	3,600	25°
△	☺	65MR16Q/10°/NSP/B	58559	12		n/a	3,500		3,000k	100	12,500	10°
											75	**Watt**
△	☺	75MR16Q/40°/FL/B	58599	12		n/a	3,500		3,000k	100	2,000	40°
△	☺	75MR16Q/25°/NFL/B	58598	12		n/a	3,500		3,000k	100	3,800	25°
△	☺	75MR16Q/11°/NSP/B	58597	12		n/a	3,500		3,000k	100	12,000	11°

Halogen Low Voltage Tru-Aim Brilliant Cover Glass

		Lamp Description	Part Number	Volts	Lumens	L/W	Hours	MOL	Color Temp	CRI	Candle Power	Beam Angle
											20	**Watt**
△	☺	20MR16Q/35°/FL/B/C	58570	12		n/a	2,000		3,000k	100	600	35°
△	☺	20MR16Q/8°/NSP/B/C	58569	12		n/a	2,000		3,000k	100	4,400	8°
											50	**Watt**
△	☺	50MR16Q/35°/FL/B/C	58575	12		n/a	3,500		3,000k	100	1,800	35°
△	☺	50MR16Q/11°/NSP/B/C	58574	12		n/a	3,500		3,000k	100	10,000	11°

Halogen Low Voltage Tru-Aim UV Stop

		Lamp Description	Part Number	Volts	Lumens	L/W	Hours	MOL	Color Temp	CRI	Candle Power	Beam Angle
											20	**Watt**
△	☺	20MR16Q/60°/VWFL/T/C	58562	12		n/a	3,000		3,000k	100	350	60°
△	☺	20MR16Q/40°/FL/T/C	58551	12		n/a	3,000		3,000k	100	700	40°
△	☺	20MR16Q/10°/NSP/T/C	58550	12		n/a	3,000		3,000k	100	5,000	10°
											35	**Watt**
△	☺	35MR16Q/60°/VWFL/T/C	58552	12		n/a	4,000		3,000k	100	650	60°
△	☺	35MR16Q/40°/FL/T/C	58557	12		n/a	4,000		3,000k	100	1,250	40°
△	☺	35MR16Q/10°/NSP/T/C	58558	12		n/a	4,000		3,000k	100	8,300	10°
											50	**Watt**
△	☺	50MR16Q/60°/VWFL/T/C	58553	12		n/a	4,000		3,000k	100	1,000	60°
△	☺	50MR16Q/40°/FL/T/C	58554	12		n/a	4,000		3,000k	100	2,000	40°
△	☺	50MR16Q/25°/NFL/T/C	58555	12		n/a	4,000		3,000k	100	3,200	25°
△	☺	50MR16Q/10°/NSP/T/C	58556	12		n/a	4,000		3,000k	100	11,500	10°

AR70

Halogen Low Voltage Aluminum Reflector

		Lamp Description	Part Number	Volts	Lumens	L/W	Hours	MOL	Color Temp	CRI	Candle Power	Beam Angle
											20	**Watt**
△	☺	20AR70/25°/FL	59012	12		n/a	2,000		3,000k	100	850	25°
△	☺	20AR70/8°/SP	59013	12		n/a	2,000		3,000k	100	7,000	8°
											50	**Watt**
△	☺	50AR70/25°/FL	59016	12		n/a	2,000		3,000k	100	2,000	25°
△	☺	50AR70/8°/SP	59017	12		n/a	2,000		3,000k	100	15,000	8°

FLUORESCENT

Bulb Diameters

Regarding fluorescent lamps, the bulb diameter is expressed in **eighths** of an inch just like the incandescent lamps. Refer to the description on bulb diameters in figure A-3 for more information.

A typical 4' fluorescent tube is known as a T12. The **T** stands for **tube** and the **12** stands for 12/8 of an inch in diameter, or 1 1/2 inches. A T5 lamp used in under cabinet lighting is 5/8 of an inch in diameter.

MOL (Maximum Overall Length)

From the crown of the lamp to the tip of its screw in, or plug in base is the MOL or maximum overall length of the lamp. See figure A.3.

A 4' tubular fluorescent lamp is known as an F40T12. The F40 stands for **Fluorescent 40 Watts**. F40 is used to indicate the lamps length and the wattage when T12 lamps were 10 watts per foot. However, with the more energy efficient 34 watt, 4 foot fluorescent tubes, the designation, F40, now refers only to the lamps length.

Appendix Conventions (Fluorescent)

EPACT Compliance

Ⓔ - Efficiency approved according to new federal EPACT standards.

△ - Either exempt from EPACT, or EPACT guidelines do not apply (i.e., compact fluorescent).

Color Symbols

☺ - Means the lamp has a CRI of 80 or higher and a color temperature between 3,000k and 3,600k. See Chapter 2.

☺ - Means the lamp has a CRI over 70 and a color temperature between 3,000k and 3,700k. See Chapter 2.

Look for lamps with one of these two symbol pairs for best color and efficiency!

Organization by Manufacturer

Lamps listed in this Appendix represent the most commonly used lamps for residential interior use. They have been grouped by lamp family for convenience and then subdivided by the three major manufacturers, GE, Phillips, and Sylvania/Osram.

This should make finding a lamp exceedingly easier than leafing through full line catalogues featuring thousands of lamps that are not applicable. It should reduce that mess on your desk a bit as well.

Lamp Shapes (Not Actual Sizes)

Bulb Shapes (Not Actual Sizes)

The size and shape of a bulb is designated by a letter or letters followed by a number. The letter indicates the shape of the bulb while the number indicates the diameter of the bulb in eighths of an inch. For example, "T-12" indicates a tubular shaped bulb having a diameter of $^{12}/_8$ or $1^1/_2$ inches. The following illustrations show some of the more popular bulb shapes and sizes.

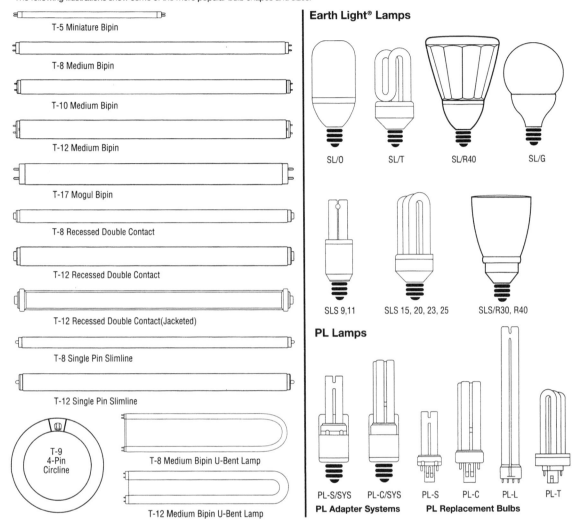

T-5 Miniature Bipin

T-8 Medium Bipin

T-10 Medium Bipin

T-12 Medium Bipin

T-17 Mogul Bipin

T-8 Recessed Double Contact

T-12 Recessed Double Contact

T-12 Recessed Double Contact(Jacketed)

T-8 Single Pin Slimline

T-12 Single Pin Slimline

T-9 4-Pin Circline

T-8 Medium Bipin U-Bent Lamp

T-12 Medium Bipin U-Bent Lamp

Earth Light® Lamps

SL/O   SL/T   SL/R40   SL/G

SLS 9,11   SLS 15, 20, 23, 25   SLS/R30, R40

PL Lamps

PL-S/SYS   PL-C/SYS   PL-S   PL-C   PL-L   PL-T

PL Adapter Systems   **PL Replacement Bulbs**

Figure A.4   *Fluorescent Lamp Shapes*

Courtesy *Phillips*

Compact Fluorescent Cross-Reference		
GE	**PHILIPS**	**OSRAM/SYLVANIA**
2D	–	–
Biax	PL	DULUX S/Twin Tube
Compax, Biax	Earthlight, PL	DULUX EL/Electronic
Double Biax	PL-C	DULUX /Double Twin Tube
High Lumen Biax	PL-L	DULUX /L
Oct	–	–
Triple Biax	PL-T	DULUX T/E

Figure A.5   *Compact Fluorescent Cross-Reference*

Base Types (Not Actual Sizes)

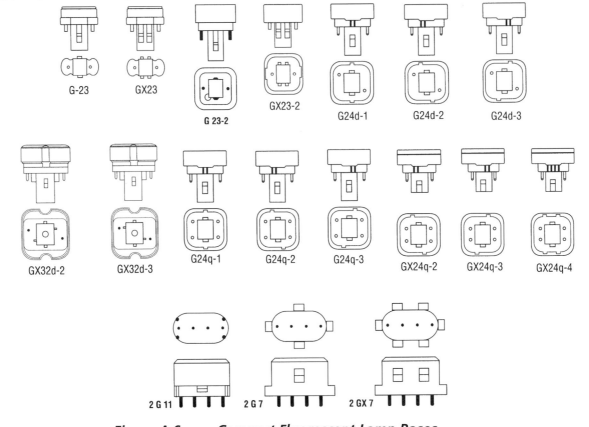

G-23   GX23

G 23-2

GX23-2

G24d-1   G24d-2   G24d-3

GX32d-2   GX32d-3   G24q-1   G24q-2   G24q-3   GX24q-2   GX24q-3   GX24q-4

2 G 11   2 G 7   2 GX 7

Figure A.6   ***Compact Fluorescent Lamp Bases***

Courtesy ***Phillips & GE***

Fluorescent Color Cross-Reference		
GE	**PHILIPS**	**OSRAM/SYLVANIA**
SP30	Spec 30	D30
SP35	Spec 35	D35
SP41	Spec 41	D41
SPX30	30U	D830
SPX35	35U	D835
SPX41	41U	D841
C50	C50	DSGN50
SPX27	27	827
SW	WWX	WWX

Figure A.7   ***Fluorescent Color Cross-Reference***

General Electric

Linear Fluorescent

	Lamp Description	Part Number	Base	L/W	Hours	MOL	Color Temp	CRI	Lumens
T 5									
	Linear Fluorescent Common								
								4	**Watt**
	F4T5/CW	10004	Mini-BiPin G5	34	6,000	6"	4,150k	62	135
								6	**Watt**
	F6T5/CW	10032	Mini-BiPin G5	49	7,500	9"	4,150k	62	295
								8	**Watt**
	F8T5/WW	10064	Mini-BiPin G5	51	7,500	12"	3,000k	52	410
	F8T5/CW	10059	Mini-BiPin G5	50	7,500	12"	4,150k	62	400
								13	**Watt**
	F13T5/WW	10089	Mini-BiPin G5	67	7,500	21"	3,000k	52	870
	F13T5/CW	10086	Mini-BiPin G5	65	7,500	21"	4,150k	62	850
T 8									
	Linear Fluorescent Common								
								13	**Watt**
	F13T8/CW	10098	Med-BiPin G13	43	7,500	12"	4,150k	62	565
								14	**Watt**
	F14T8/CW	10104	Med-BiPin G13	49	7,500	15"	4,150k	62	685
								15	**Watt**
	F15T8/WW	10147	Med-BiPin G13	56	7,500	18"	3,000k	52	845
	F15T8/CW	10142	Med-BiPin G13	55	7,500	18"	4,150k	62	825
	F15T8/C50 Chroma 50	38185	Med-BiPin G13	41	7,500	18"	5,000k	90	620
								30	**Watt**
	F30T8/WW	23492	Med-BiPin G13	75	7,500	36"	3,000k	52	2,250
☺	F30T8/KB Kitchen & Bath	22747	Med-BiPin G13	71	7,500	36"	3,000k	75	2,125
☺	F30T8/N Natural	10328	Med-BiPin G13	50	7,500	36"	3,700k	90	1,500
	F30T8/CW	10316	Med-BiPin G13	73	7,500	36"	4,150k	62	2,175
	Linear Fluorescent SP								
								15	**Watt**
☺	F15T8/SP30	17910	Med-BiPin G13	63	7,500	18"	3,000k	75	940
☺	F15T8/SP35	17911	Med-BiPin G13	63	7,500	18"	3,500k	75	940
	F15T8/SP41	19643	Med-BiPin G13	63	7,500	18"	4,100k	75	940
	Linear Fluorescent SPX								
								15	**Watt**
☺	F15T8/SPX30	19644	Med-BiPin G13	67	7,500	18"	3,000k	82	1,000
☺	F15T8/SPX35	19645	Med-BiPin G13	67	7,500	18"	3,500k	82	1,000
	F15T8/SPX41	19646	Med-BiPin G13	67	7,500	18"	4,100k	80	1,000
	F15T8/SPX50	10756	Med-BiPin G13	63	7,500	18"	5,000k	80	940
								30	**Watt**
☺	F30T8/SPX30	16323	Med-BiPin G13	77	7,500	36"	3,000k	82	2,300

General Electric

Linear Fluorescent

		Lamp Description	Part Number	Base	L/W	Hours	MOL	Color Temp	CRI	Lumens
T12										
		Linear Fluorescent Common							**25**	**Watt**
		F48"/25W/UTSL Utility Shoplite	14445	Med-BiPin G13	74	12,000	48"	4,150k	62	1,860
									34	**Watt**
Ⓔ		F40WW/RS/WM	13821	Med-BiPin G13	81	20,000	48"	3,000k	52	2,750
Ⓔ		F40CW/RS/WM	13803	Med-BiPin G13	78	20,000	48"	4,150k	62	2,650
Ⓔ		F40LW/RS/WM Lite White	13822	Med-BiPin G13	83	20,000	48"	4,200k	49	2,825
		F40/C50/RS/WM Chroma 50	19217	Med-BiPin G13	59	20,000	48"	5,000k	90	2,000
									40	**Watt**
Ⓔ	☺	F40KB Kitchen & Bath	21323	Med-BiPin G13	80	20,000	48"	3,000k	70	3,200
		Linear Fluorescent SP								
									34	**Watt**
Ⓔ	☺	F40SP30/RS/WM	14200	Med-BiPin G13	81	20,000	48"	3,000k	70	2,750
Ⓔ	☺	F40SP35/RS/WM	13807	Med-BiPin G13	81	20,000	48"	3,500k	73	2,750
Ⓔ		F40SP41/RS/WM	13809	Med-BiPin G13	81	20,000	48"	4,100k	72	2,750
		Linear Fluorescent SPX								
									34	**Watt**
Ⓔ	☺	F40SPX30/RS/WM	14627	Med-BiPin G13	85	20,000	48"	3,000k	82	2,900
Ⓔ	☺	F40SPX35/RS/WM	14628	Med-BiPin G13	85	20,000	48"	3,500k	82	2,900
Ⓔ		F40SPX41/RS/WM	14811	Med-BiPin G13	85	20,000	48"	4,100k	80	2,900
Ⓔ		F40SPX50/RS/WM	23459	Med-BiPin G13	79	20,000	48"	5,000k	80	2,700

Phillips

Linear Fluorescent

Lamp Description	Part Number	Base	L/W	Hours	MOL	Color Temp	CRI	Lumens
T 5								
Linear Fluorescent Common								
							4	**Watt**
F4T5/CW	33236-1	Mini-BiPin G5	34	6,000	6"	4,100k	62	135
							6	**Watt**
F6T5/CW	33241-1	Mini-BiPin G5	49	7,500	9"	4,100k	62	295
							8	**Watt**
F8T5/WW	33252-8	Mini-BiPin G5	50	7,500	12"	3,000k	53	400
F8T5/CW	33247-8	Mini-BiPin G5	50	7,500	12"	4,100k	62	400
							13	**Watt**
F13T5/CW	33253-6	Mini-BiPin G5	63	7,500	21"	4,100k	62	820
Linear Fluorescent Ultralume								
							8	**Watt**
☺ F8T5/30U	20702-7	Mini-BiPin G5	56	7,500	12"	3,000k	85	450
							13	**Watt**
☺ F13T5/30U	20703-5	Mini-BiPin G5	77	7,500	21"	3,000k	85	1,000
T 8								
Linear Fluorescent Common								
							13	**Watt**
F13T8/CW	25910-1	Med-BiPin G13	38	7,500	12"	4,100k	62	500
							15	**Watt**
F15T8/WW	25946-5	Med-BiPin G13	58	7,500	18"	3,000k	53	870
F15T8/CW	25936-6	Med-BiPin G13	58	7,500	18"	4,100k	62	870
F15T8/C50 ColorTone 50	34286-5	Med-BiPin G13	39	7,500	18"	5,000k	92	590
							30	**Watt**
F30T8/WW	26058-8	Med-BiPin G13	75	7,500	36"	3,000k	53	2,260
☺ F30T8/N	20039-4	Med-BiPin G13	50	7,500	36"	3,700k	90	1,500
F30T8/CW	26050-5	Med-BiPin G13	73	7,500	36"	4,100k	62	2,200
Linear Fluorescent SPEC								
							15	**Watt**
☺ F15T8/SPEC35	25853-3	Med-BiPin G13	63	7,500	18"	3,500k	73	940
Linear Fluorescent Ultralume								
							15	**Watt**
☺ F15T8/30U	31515-0	Med-BiPin G13	67	7,500	18"	3,000k	85	1,000
F15T8/41U	31516-8	Med-BiPin G13	67	7,500	18"	4,100k	85	1,000
F15T8/50U	31519-2	Med-BiPin G13	67	7,500	18"	5,000k	85	1,000

Phillips

Linear Fluorescent

		Lamp Description	Part Number	Base	L/W	Hours	MOL	Color Temp	CRI	Lumens
T12										
		Linear Fluorescent Common								
									34	**Watt**
Ⓔ	☺	F40SF/RS/EW Softone	21316-5	Med-BiPin G13	82	20,000	48"	3,000k	70	2,800
Ⓔ		F40WW/RS/EW	29471-0	Med-BiPin G13	79	20,000	48"	3,000k	53	2,700
Ⓔ		F40CW/RS/EW	28484-4	Med-BiPin G13	78	20,000	48"	4,100k	62	2,650
Ⓔ		F40LW/RS/EW Lite White	28534-6	Med-BiPin G13	81	20,000	48"	4,100k	51	2,750
		F40CWX/RS/EW Cool White Deluxe	28511-4	Med-BiPin G13	57	20,000	48"	4,200k	89	1,925
		Linear Fluorescent SPEC								
									34	**Watt**
Ⓔ	☺	F40SPEC30/RS/EW	31553-1	Med-BiPin G13	82	20,000	48"	3,000k	70	2,800
Ⓔ	☺	F40SPEC35/RS/EW	37992-5	Med-BiPin G13	82	20,000	48"	3,500k	73	2,800
Ⓔ		F40SPEC41/RS/EW	31546-5	Med-BiPin G13	82	20,000	48"	4,100k	70	2,800
		Linear Fluorescent Ultralume								
									34	**Watt**
Ⓔ	☺	F40/30U/RS/EW	31532-5	Med-BiPin G13	85	20,000	48"	3,000k	85	2,900
Ⓔ	☺	F40/35U/RS/EW	38004-8	Med-BiPin G13	85	20,000	48"	3,500k	85	2,900
Ⓔ		F40/41U/RS/EW	31533-3	Med-BiPin G13	85	20,000	48"	4,100k	85	2,900
Ⓔ		F40/50U/RS/EW	31535-8	Med-BiPin G13	85	20,000	48"	5,000k	85	2,880

Sylvania-Osram

Linear Fluorescent

Lamp Description	Part Number	Base	L/W	Hours	MOL	Color Temp	CRI	Lumens
T 5								
Linear Fluorescent Common								
							4	**Watt**
F4T5/CW	20416	Mini–BiPin G5	34	6,000	6"	4,200k	62	135
							6	**Watt**
F6T5/WW	20617	Mini–BiPin G5	46	7,500	9"	3,000k	52	275
F6T5/W	20621	Mini–BiPin G5	46	7,500	9"	3,450k	57	275
F6T5/CW	20616	Mini–BiPin G5	45	7,500	9"	4,200k	62	270
							8	**Watt**
F8T5/WW	20817	Mini–BiPin G5	50	7,500	12"	3,000k	52	400
F8T5/W	20821	Mini–BiPin G5	50	7,500	12"	3,450k	57	400
F8T5/CWX Cool White Deluxe	20837	Mini–BiPin G5	34	7,500	12"	4,100k	89	270
F8T5/CW	20816	Mini–BiPin G5	49	7,500	12"	4,200k	62	390
							13	**Watt**
F13T5/WW	21317	Mini–BiPin G5	68	7,500	21"	3,000k	52	880
F13T5/CW	21316	Mini–BiPin G5	66	7,500	21"	4,200k	62	860
T 8								
Linear Fluorescent Common								
							13	**Watt**
F13T8/CW	21766	Med–BiPin G13	41	7,500	12"	4,200k	62	530
							14	**Watt**
F14T8/CW	21486	Med–BiPin G13	53	7,500	15"	4,200k	62	740
							15	**Watt**
F15T8/WW	21701	Med–BiPin G13	56	7,500	18"	3,000k	52	845
☺ F15T8/N Natural	21682	Med–BiPin G13	37	7,500	18"	3,600k	86	560
F15T8/CWX Cool White Deluxe	21627	Med–BiPin G13	40	7,500	18"	4,100k	89	600
							22	**Watt**
F22T8/CW	23026	Med–BiPin G13	70	7,500	26"	4,200k	62	1,530
							30	**Watt**
F30T8/WW	23701	Med–BiPin G13	72	7,500	36"	3,000k	52	2,150
☺ F30T8/N Natural	23182	Med–BiPin G13	50	7,500	36"	3,600k	86	1,500
F30T8/CWX Cool White Deluxe	23127	Med–BiPin G13	52	7,500	36"	4,100k	89	1,550
F30T8/CW	23116	Med–BiPin G13	73	7,500	36"	4,200k	62	2,180
Linear Fluorescent Designer								
							15	**Watt**
☺ F15T8/D30	21654	Med–BiPin G13	60	7,500	18"	3,000k	70	900
							30	**Watt**
☺ F30T8/D30	23138	Med–BiPin G13	79	7,500	36"	3,000k	70	2,360
Linear Fluorescent Designer 800								
							15	**Watt**
☺ F15T8/D830	21610	Med–BiPin G13	61	7,500	18"	3,000k	80	920

Sylvania-Osram

Linear Fluorescent

		Lamp Description	Part Number	Base	L/W	Hours	MOL	Color Temp	CRI	Lumens
T12										
		Linear Fluorescent Common								
								34		**Watt**
	☺	F40/SOFT WHITE/ES/12	24752	Med-BiPin G13	55	20,000	48"	2,900k	82	1,880
Ⓔ		F40WW/SS	24595	Med-BiPin G13	81	20,000	48"	3,000k	52	2,750
Ⓔ		F40W/SS White	24591	Med-BiPin G13	81	20,000	48"	3,450k	57	2,750
		F40/CWX/SS Cool White Deluxe	24588	Med-BiPin G13	57	20,000	48"	4,100k	89	1,925
Ⓔ		F40/LW/SS Lite White	24590	Med-BiPin G13	83	20,000	48"	4,150k	48	2,825
Ⓔ		F40/CW/SS	24594	Med-BiPin G13	79	20,000	48"	4,200k	62	2,700
		Linear Fluorescent Designer								
								34		**Watt**
Ⓔ	☺	F40/D30/SS	24580	Med-BiPin G13	82	20,000	48"	3,000k	70	2,800
Ⓔ	☺	F40/D35/SS	24585	Med-BiPin G13	82	20,000	48"	3,500k	70	2,800
Ⓔ		F40/D41/SS	24593	Med-BiPin G13	82	20,000	48"	4,100k	70	2,800
		Linear Fluorescent Designer 800								
								34		**Watt**
Ⓔ	☺	F40/D830/SS	24589	Med-BiPin G13	85	20,000	48"	3,000k	80	2,900
Ⓔ	☺	F40/D835/SS	24581	Med-BiPin G13	85	20,000	48"	3,500k	80	2,900
Ⓔ		F40/D841/SS	24586	Med-BiPin G13	85	20,000	48"	4,100k	80	2,900

General Electric

Compact Fluorescent

		Lamp Description	Part Number	Base	L/W	Hours	MOL	Color Temp	CRI	Lumens
TWIN										
		Compact Fluorescent Biax								
										5 Watt
△		F5BX/SPX27/827	19355	2 Pin G23	50	10,000	4.2"	2,700k	82	250
△	☺	F5BX/SPX35/835	29960	2 Pin G23	50	10,000	4.2"	3,500k	82	250
△		F5BX/SPX41/840	29961	2 Pin G23	50	10,000	4.2"	4,100k	82	250
										7 Watt
△		F7BX/SPX27/827	14115	2 Pin G23	57	10,000	5.3"	2,700k	82	400
△	☺	F7BX/SPX35/835	17084	2 Pin G23	57	10,000	5.3"	3,500k	82	400
		F7BX/SPX41/840	20432	2 Pin G23	57	10,000	5.3"	4,100k	80	400
										9 Watt
△		F9BX/SPX27/827	14117	2 Pin G23	67	10,000	6.6"	2,700k	82	600
△	☺	F9BX/SPX35/835	17086	2 Pin G23	67	10,000	6.6"	3,500k	82	600
		F9BX/SPX41/840	20431	2 Pin G23	67	10,000	6.6"	4,100k	80	600
										13 Watt
△		F13BX/SPX27/827	14650	2 Pin GX23	63	10,000	7.5"	2,700k	82	825
△	☺	F13BX/SPX30/830	17612	2 Pin GX23	63	10,000	7.5"	3,000k	82	825
△	☺	F13BX/SPX35/835	17048	2 Pin GX23	63	10,000	7.5"	3,500k	82	825
		F13BX/SPX41/840	20434	2 Pin GX23	63	10,000	7.5"	4,100k	80	825

General Electric

Compact Fluorescent

		Lamp Description	Part Number	Base	L/W	Hours	MOL	Color Temp	CRI	Lumens
DOUBLE TWIN										
		Compact Fluorescent Double Biax								
									9	**Watt**
△		F9DBX23T4/SPX27	12409	2 Pin G23-2	61	10,000	4.3"	2,700k	82	550
									10	**Watt**
△		F10DBXT4/SPX27	12872	2 Pin G24d-1	55	10,000	4.3"	2,700k	82	550
△	☺	F10DBXT4/SPX30	12874	2 Pin G24d-1	55	10,000	4.3"	3,000k	82	550
△	☺	F10DBXT4/SPX35	12875	2 Pin G24d-1	55	10,000	4.3"	3,500k	82	550
									13	**Watt**
△		F13DBXT4/SPX27	18557	2 Pin G24d-1	69	10,000	5.3"	2,700k	82	900
△	☺	F13DBXT4/SPX30	12956	2 Pin G24d-1	69	10,000	5.3"	3,000k	82	900
△	☺	F13DBXT4/SPX35	18559	2 Pin G24d-1	69	10,000	5.3"	3,500k	82	900
△		F13DBX23T4/SPX27	18844	2 Pin GX23-2	66	10,000	4.7"	2,700k	82	860
△	☺	F13DBX23T4/SPX30	10574	2 Pin GX23-2	66	10,000	4.7"	3,000k	82	860
△	☺	F13DBX23T4/SPX35	18556	2 Pin GX23-2	66	10,000	4.7"	3,500k	82	860
△		F13DBX23T4/SPX41	20531	2 Pin GX23-2	66	10,000	4.7"	4,100k	82	860
									18	**Watt**
△		F18DBXT4/SPX27	12860	2 Pin G24d-2	64	10,000	6.1"	2,700k	82	1,160
△	☺	F18DBXT4/SPX30	12861	2 Pin G24d-2	64	10,000	6.1"	3,000k	82	1,160
△	☺	F18DBXT4/SPX35	12863	2 Pin G24d-2	64	10,000	6.1"	3,500k	82	1,160
△		F18DBXT4/SPX41	12864	2 Pin G24d-2	64	10,000	6.1"	4,100k	82	1,160
									26	**Watt**
△		F26DBXT4/SPX27	18566	2 Pin G24d-3	65	10,000	6.7"	2,700k	82	1,700
△	☺	F26DBXT4/SPX30	10578	2 Pin G24d-3	65	10,000	6.7"	3,000k	82	1,700
△	☺	F26DBXT4/SPX35	18567	2 Pin G24d-3	65	10,000	6.7"	3,500k	82	1,700
△		F26DBXT4/SPX41	20534	2 Pin G24d-3	65	10,000	6.7"	4,100k	82	1,700
		Compact Fluorescent Double Biax Electronic/Dimming								
									10	**Watt**
△		F10DBX/SPX27/4P	30031	4 Pin G24q-1	55	10,000	4"	2,700k	82	550
△	☺	F10DBX/SPX30/4P	12877	4 Pin G24q-1	55	10,000	4"	3,000k	82	550
△	☺	F10DBX/SPX35/4P	30032	4 Pin G24q-1	55	10,000	4"	3,500k	82	550
△		F10DBX/SPX41/4P	30034	4 Pin G24q-1	55	10,000	4"	4,100k	82	550
									13	**Watt**
△		F13DBX/SPX27/4P	30035	4 Pin G24q-1	69	10,000	5.1"	2,700k	82	900
△	☺	F13DBX/SPX30/4P	10580	4 Pin G24q-1	69	10,000	5.1"	3,000k	82	900
△	☺	F13DBX/SPX35/4P	30037	4 Pin G24q-1	69	10,000	5.1"	3,500k	82	900
△		F13DBX/SPX41/4P	30038	4 Pin G24q-1	69	10,000	5.1"	4,100k	82	900
									18	**Watt**
△		F18DBX/SPX27/4P	12865	4 Pin G24q-2	64	10,000	5.8"	2,700k	82	1,160
△	☺	F18DBX/SPX30/4P	12866	4 Pin G24q-2	64	10,000	5.8"	3,000k	82	1,160
△	☺	F18DBX/SPX35/4P	12869	4 Pin G24q-2	64	10,000	5.8"	3,500k	82	1,160
△		F18DBX/SPX41/4P	12870	4 Pin G24q-2	64	10,000	5.8"	4,100k	82	1,160
									26	**Watt**
△		F26DBX/SPX27/4P	30042	4 Pin G24q-3	65	10,000	6.4"	2,700k	82	1,700
△	☺	F26DBX/SPX30/4P	10610	4 Pin G24q-3	65	10,000	6.4"	3,000k	82	1,700
△	☺	F26DBX/SPX35/4P	30043	4 Pin G24q-3	65	10,000	6.4"	3,500k	82	1,700
△		F26DBX/SPX41/4P	30044	4 Pin G24q-3	65	10,000	6.4"	4,100k	82	1,700

General Electric   ## Compact Fluorescent

		Lamp Description	Part Number	Base	L/W	Hours	MOL	Color Temp	CRI	Lumens
TRIPLE TWIN										
		Compact Fluorescent Triple Biax Electronic/Dimming								
									13	**Watt**
△		F13TBX/SPX27/4P	11982	4 Pin GX24q-1	65	10,000	4.2"	2,700k	82	840
△	☺	F13TBX/SPX30/4P	11983	4 Pin GX24q-1	65	10,000	4.2"	3,000k	82	840
△	☺	F13TBX/SPX35/4P	11984	4 Pin GX24q-1	65	10,000	4.2"	3,500k	82	840
△		F13TBX/SPX41/4P	12816	4 Pin GX24q-1	65	10,000	4.2"	4,100k	82	840
									18	**Watt**
△		F18TBX/SPX27/4P	10449	4 Pin GX24q-2	62	10,000	4.6"	2,700k	82	1,120
△	☺	F18TBX/SPX30/4P	11986	4 Pin GX24q-2	62	10,000	4.6"	3,000k	82	1,120
△	☺	F18TBX/SPX35/4P	11987	4 Pin GX24q-2	62	10,000	4.6"	3,500k	82	1,120
△		F18TBX/SPX41/4P	12817	4 Pin GX24q-2	62	10,000	4.6"	4,100k	82	1,120
									26	**Watt**
△		F26TBX/SPX27/4P	12278	4 Pin GX24q-3	62	10,000	5.2"	2,700k	82	1,610
△	☺	F26TBX/SPX30/4P	12480	4 Pin GX24q-3	62	10,000	5.2"	3,000k	82	1,610
△	☺	F26TBX/SPX35/4P	12488	4 Pin GX24q-3	62	10,000	5.2"	3,500k	82	1,610
△		F26TBX/SPX41/4P	12821	4 Pin GX24q-3	62	10,000	5.2"	4,100k	82	1,610
									32	**Watt**
△		F32TBX/SPX27/4P	12781	4 Pin GX24q-3	69	10,000	5.8"	2,700k	82	2,200
△	☺	F32TBX/SPX30/4P	12489	4 Pin GX24q-3	69	10,000	5.8"	3,000k	82	2,200
△	☺	F32TBX/SPX35/4P	12490	4 Pin GX24q-3	69	10,000	5.8"	3,500k	82	2,200
△		F32TBX/SPX41/4P	12823	4 Pin GX24q-3	69	10,000	5.8"	4,100k	82	2,200

Phillips

Compact Fluorescent

	Lamp Description	Part Number	Base	L/W	Hours	MOL	Color Temp	CRI	Lumens
TWIN									
	Compact Fluorescent PL								
								5	**Watt**
△	PL-S 5W/27	33233-8	2 Pin G23	50	10,000	4 1/8"	2,700k	82	250
								7	**Watt**
△	PL-S 7W/27	34256-8	2 Pin G23	57	10,000	5 1/4"	2,700k	82	400
△ ☺	PL-S 7W/35	32780-9	2 Pin G23	57	10,000	5 1/4"	3,500k	82	400
△	PL-S 7W/41	33869-9	2 Pin G23	57	10,000	5 1/4"	4,100k	82	400
								9	**Watt**
△	PL-S 9W/27	34257-6	2 Pin G23	67	10,000	6 1/2"	2,700k	82	600
△ ☺	PL-S 9W/35	32786-6	2 Pin G23	67	10,000	6 1/2"	3,500k	82	600
△	PL-S 9W/41	33870-7	2 Pin G23	67	10,000	6 1/2"	4,100k	82	600
								13	**Watt**
△	PL-S 13W/27	34258-4	2 Pin GX23	69	10,000	7 3/8"	2,700k	82	900
△ ☺	PL-S 13W/30	20986-6	2 Pin GX23	69	10,000	7 3/8"	3,000k	82	900
△ ☺	PL-S 13W/35	32788-2	2 Pin GX23	69	10,000	7 3/8"	3,500k	82	900
△	PL-S 13W/41	30783-5	2 Pin GX23	69	10,000	7 3/8"	4,100k	82	900
DOUBLE TWIN									
	Compact Fluorescent PL-C								
								13	**Watt**
△	PL-C 13W/27	33943-2	2 Pin G24d-1	69	10,000	5 1/2"	2,700k	82	900
△ ☺	PL-C 13W/30	20434-7	2 Pin G24d-1	69	10,000	5 1/2"	3,000k	82	900
△	PL-C 13W/27/USA	24546-4	2 Pin GX23-2	66	10,000	4 5/8"	2,700k	82	860
△ ☺	PL-C 13W/30/USA	20435-4	2 Pin GX23-2	66	10,000	4 5/8"	3,000k	82	860
△ ☺	PL-C 13W/35/USA	34005-9	2 Pin GX23-2	66	10,000	4 5/8"	3,500k	82	860
△	PL-C 13W/41/USA	33954-9	2 Pin GX23-2	66	10,000	4 5/8"	4,100k	82	860
								18	**Watt**
△	PL-C 18W/27	33944-0	2 Pin G24d-2	69	10,000	6"	2,700k	82	1,250
△ ☺	PL-C 18W/30	20436-2	2 Pin G24d-2	69	10,000	6"	3,000k	82	1,250
△ ☺	PL-C 18W/35	34008-3	2 Pin G24d-2	69	10,000	6"	3,500k	82	1,250
△	PL-C 18W/41	34011-7	2 Pin G24d-2	69	10,000	6"	4,100k	82	1,250
								26	**Watt**
△	PL-C 26W/27	34953-0	2 Pin G24d-3	69	10,000	6 7/8"	2,700k	82	1,800
△ ☺	PL-C 26W/30	20444-6	2 Pin G24d-3	69	10,000	6 7/8"	3,000k	82	1,800
△ ☺	PL-C 26W/35	34009-1	2 Pin G24d-3	69	10,000	6 7/8"	3,500k	82	1,800
△	PL-C 26W/41	34012-5	2 Pin G24d-3	69	10,000	6 7/8"	4,100k	82	1,800
	Compact Fluorescent PL-C Electronic/Dimming								
								13	**Watt**
△	PL-C 13W/27/4P	31511-9	4 Pin G24q-1	69	10,000	5 1/8"	2,700k	82	900
								18	**Watt**
△	PL-C 18W/27/4P	31492-2	4 Pin G24q-2	69	10,000	5 5/8"	2,700k	82	1,250
								26	**Watt**
△	PL-C 26W/27/4P	31512-7	4 Pin G24q-3	69	10,000	6 1/2"	2,700k	82	1,800
△ ☺	PL-C 26W/35/4P	34028-1	4 Pin G24q-3	69	10,000	6 1/2"	3,500k	82	1,800
△	PL-C 26W/41/4P	34031-5	4 Pin G24q-3	69	10,000	6 1/2"	4,100k	82	1,800

Phillips

Compact Fluorescent

		Lamp Description	Part Number	Base	L/W	Hours	MOL	Color Temp	CRI	Lumens
TRIPLE TWIN										
		Compact Fluorescent PL-T Electronic/Dimming								
									18	**Watt**
△	☺	PL-T 18W/30/4P	22224-0	4 Pin GX24q-2	53	10,000	4 5/8"	3,000k	82	960
△	☺	PL-T 18W/35/4P	22231-5	4 Pin GX24q-2	53	10,000	4 5/8"	3,500k	82	960
△		PL-T 18W/41/4P	22233-1	4 Pin GX24q-2	53	10,000	4 5/8"	4,100k	82	960
									26	**Watt**
△	☺	PL-T 26W/30/4P	34741-9	4 Pin GX24q-3	55	10,000	4 7/8"	3,000k	82	1,440
△	☺	PL-T 26W/35/4P	34742-7	4 Pin GX24q-3	55	10,000	4 7/8"	3,500k	82	1,440
△		PL-T 26W/41/4P	35366-4	4 Pin GX24q-3	55	10,000	4 7/8"	4,100k	82	1,440
									32	**Watt**
△	☺	PL-T 32W/30/4P	34743-5	4 Pin GX24q-3	60	10,000	5 1/2"	3,000k	82	1,920
△	☺	PL-T 32W/35/4P	34743-3	4 Pin GX24q-3	60	10,000	5 1/2"	3,500k	82	1,920
△		PL-T 32W/41/4P	35367-2	4 Pin GX24q-3	60	10,000	5 1/2"	4,100k	82	1,920
									42	**Watt**
△	☺	PL-T 42W/30/4P	22125-9	4 Pin GX24q-4	61	10,000	6 3/8"	3,000k	82	2,560
△	☺	PL-T 42W/35/4P	22126-7	4 Pin GX24q-4	61	10,000	6 3/8"	3,500k	82	2,560
△		PL-T 42W/41/4P	22134-1	4 Pin GX24q-4	61	10,000	6 3/8"	4,100k	82	2,560

Sylvania-Osram   Compact Fluorescent

	Lamp Description	Part Number	Base	L/W	Hours	MOL	Color Temp	CRI	Lumens
TWIN									
Compact Fluorescent Dulux S									
									5 Watt
△	CF5DS/827	20325	2 Pin G23	46	10,000	4.2"	2,700k	82	230
△	CF5DS/841	20303	2 Pin G23	46	10,000	4.2"	4,100k	82	230
									7 Watt
△	CF7DS/827	20327	2 Pin G23	57	10,000	5.3"	2,700k	82	400
△ ☺	CF7DS/835	20310	2 Pin G23	57	10,000	5.3"	3,500k	82	400
△	CF7DS/841	20304	2 Pin G23	57	10,000	5.3"	4,100k	82	400
									9 Watt
△	CF9DS/827	20329	2 Pin G23	64	10,000	6.5"	2,700k	82	580
△ ☺	CF9DS/835	20333	2 Pin G23	64	10,000	6.5"	3,500k	82	580
△	CF9DS/841	20305	2 Pin G23	64	10,000	6.5"	4,100k	82	580
									13 Watt
△	CF13DS/827	20331	2 Pin GX23	62	10,000	7.1"	2,700k	82	800
△ ☺	CF13DS/830	20283	2 Pin GX23	62	10,000	7.1"	3,000k	82	800
△ ☺	CF13DS/835	20335	2 Pin GX23	62	10,000	7.1"	3,500k	82	800
△	CF13DS/841	20306	2 Pin GX23	62	10,000	7.1"	4,100k	82	800
Compact Fluorescent Dulux S/E Electronic/Dimming									
									5 Watt
△	CF5DS/E/827	20311	4 Pin 2G7	46	10,000	3.4"	2,700k	82	230
△	CF5DS/E/841	20315	4 Pin 2G7	46	10,000	3.4"	4,100k	82	230
									7 Watt
△	CF7DS/E/827	20312	4 Pin 2G7	57	10,000	4.5"	2,700k	82	400
△	CF7DS/E/841	20316	4 Pin 2G7	57	10,000	4.5"	4,100k	82	400
									9 Watt
△	CF9DS/E/827	20313	4 Pin 2G7	64	10,000	5.7"	2,700k	82	580
△	CF9DS/E/841	20317	4 Pin 2G7	64	10,000	5.7"	4,100k	82	580
									13 Watt
△	C13DS/E/827	20314	4 Pin 2GX7	62	10,000	6.2"	2,700k	82	800
△ ☺	C13DS/E/830	20284	4 Pin 2GX7	62	10,000	6.2"	3,000k	82	800
△	C13DS/E/841	20318	4 Pin 2GX7	62	10,000	6.2"	4,100k	82	800

Sylvania-Osram

Compact Fluorescent

		Lamp Description	Part Number	Base	L/W	Hours	MOL	Color Temp	CRI	Lumens
DOUBLE TWIN										
Compact Fluorescent Dulux D										
									9	**Watt**
△		CF9DD/827	20689	2 Pin G23-2	58	10,000	4.3"	2,700k	82	525
△	☺	CF9DD/830	20783	2 Pin G23-2	58	10,000	4.3"	3,000k	82	525
△	☺	CF9DD/835	20690	2 Pin G23-2	58	10,000	4.3"	3,500k	82	525
									13	**Watt**
△		CF13DD/827	20691	2 Pin GX23-2	60	10,000	4.6"	2,700k	82	780
△	☺	CF13DD/830	20705	2 Pin GX23-2	60	10,000	4.6"	3,000k	82	780
△	☺	CF13DD/835	20692	2 Pin GX23-2	60	10,000	4.6"	3,500k	82	780
△		CF13DD/841	20708	2 Pin GX23-2	60	10,000	4.6"	4,100k	82	780
									18	**Watt**
△		CF18DD/827	20676	2 Pin G24d-2	69	10,000	6"	2,700k	82	1,250
△	☺	CF18DD/830	20709	2 Pin G24d-2	69	10,000	6"	3,000k	82	1,250
△	☺	CF18DD/835	20677	2 Pin G24d-2	69	10,000	6"	3,500k	82	1,250
△		CF18DD/841	20678	2 Pin G24d-2	69	10,000	6"	4,100k	82	1,250
									26	**Watt**
△		CF26DD/827	20679	2 Pin G24d-3	70	10,000	6.8"	2,700k	82	1,825
△	☺	CF26DD/830	20710	2 Pin G24d-3	70	10,000	6.8"	3,000k	82	1,825
△	☺	CF26DD/835	20680	2 Pin G24d-3	70	10,000	6.8"	3,500k	82	1,825
△		CF26DD/841	20681	2 Pin G24d-3	70	10,000	6.8"	4,100k	82	1,825
Compact Fluorescent Dulux D/E Electronic/Dimming										
									10	**Watt**
△		CF10DD/E/827	20665	4 Pin G24q-1	60	10,000	4.1"	2,700k	82	600
△	☺	CF10DD/E/835	20670	4 Pin G24q-1	60	10,000	4.1"	3,500k	82	600
△		CF10DD/E/841	20666	4 Pin G24q-1	60	10,000	4.1"	4,100k	82	600
									13	**Watt**
△		CF13DD/E/827	20682	4 Pin G24q-1	69	10,000	5.2"	2,700k	82	900
△	☺	CF13DD/E/830	20721	4 Pin G24q-1	69	10,000	5.2"	3,000k	82	900
△	☺	CF13DD/E/835	20671	4 Pin G24q-1	69	10,000	5.2"	3,500k	82	900
△		CF13DD/E/841	20667	4 Pin G24q-1	69	10,000	5.2"	4,100k	82	900
									18	**Watt**
△		CF18DD/E/827	20683	4 Pin G24q-2	69	10,000	5.8"	2,700k	82	1,250
△	☺	CF18DD/E/830	20724	4 Pin G24q-2	69	10,000	5.8"	3,000k	82	1,250
△	☺	CF18DD/E/835	20672	4 Pin G24q-2	69	10,000	5.8"	3,500k	82	1,250
△		CF18DD/E/841	20668	4 Pin G24q-2	69	10,000	5.8"	4,100k	82	1,250
									26	**Watt**
△		CF26DD/E/827	20684	4 Pin G24q-3	70	10,000	6.5"	2,700k	82	1,825
△	☺	CF26DD/E/830	20722	4 Pin G24q-3	70	10,000	6.5"	3,000k	82	1,825
△	☺	CF26DD/E/835	20673	4 Pin G24q-3	70	10,000	6.5"	3,500k	82	1,825
△		CF26DD/E/841	20669	4 Pin G24q-3	70	10,000	6.5"	4,100k	82	1,825

Sylvania-Osram   Compact Fluorescent

		Lamp Description	Part Number	Base	L/W	Hours	MOL	Color Temp	CRI	Lumens
TRIPLE TWIN										
		Compact Fluorescent Dulux T								
										18 Watt
△		CF18DT/827	20756	2 Pin GX24d-2	67	10,000	4.8"	2,700k	82	1,200
△	☺	CF18DT/830	20757	2 Pin GX24d-2	67	10,000	4.8"	3,000k	82	1,200
△	☺	CF18DT/835	20758	2 Pin GX24d-2	67	10,000	4.8"	3,500k	82	1,200
△		CF18DT/841	20759	2 Pin GX24d-2	67	10,000	4.8"	4,100k	82	1,200
										26 Watt
△		CF26DT/827	20752	2 Pin Gx24d-3	69	10,000	5.4"	2,700k	82	1,800
△	☺	CF26DT/830	20753	2 Pin Gx24d-3	69	10,000	5.4"	3,000k	82	1,800
△	☺	CF26DT/835	20754	2 Pin Gx24d-3	69	10,000	5.4"	3,500k	82	1,800
△		CF26DT/841	20755	2 Pin Gx24d-3	69	10,000	5.4"	4,100k	82	1,800
		Compact Fluorescent Dulux T/E Electronic/Dimming								
										18 Watt
△		CF18DT/E/827	20760	4 Pin GX24q-2	67	10,000	4.6"	2,700k	82	1,200
△	☺	CF18DT/E/830	20761	4 Pin GX24q-2	67	10,000	4.6"	3,000k	82	1,200
△	☺	CF18DT/E/835	20762	4 Pin GX24q-2	67	10,000	4.6"	3,500k	82	1,200
△		CF18DT/E/841	20763	4 Pin GX24q-2	67	10,000	4.6"	4,100k	82	1,200
										26 Watt
△		CF26DT/E/827	20767	4 Pin GX24q-3	69	10,000	5.2"	2,700k	82	1,800
△	☺	CF26DT/E/830	20765	4 Pin GX24q-3	69	10,000	5.2"	3,000k	82	1,800
△	☺	CF26DT/E/835	20766	4 Pin GX24q-3	69	10,000	5.2"	3,500k	82	1,800
△		CF26DT/E/841	20764	4 Pin GX24q-3	69	10,000	5.2"	4,100k	82	1,800
										32 Watt
△		CF32DT/E/827	20768	4 Pin GX24q-3	75	10,000	5.8"	2,700k	82	2,400
△	☺	CF32DT/E/830	20769	4 Pin GX24q-3	75	10,000	5.8"	3,000k	82	2,400
△	☺	CF32DT/E/835	20770	4 Pin GX24q-3	75	10,000	5.8"	3,500k	82	2,400
△		CF32DT/E/841	20771	4 Pin GX24q-3	75	10,000	5.8"	4,100k	82	2,400

APPENDIX B

CU TABLES

CU Tables *(Coefficient of Utilization)*

Coefficient of Utilization (CU) tables, just by their name, sound technically intimidating. They are really quite friendly and, when made available by a fixture manufacturer, provide necessary information about luminaires. A luminaire is the combination of a fixture, its trim, and a lamp. Remember, while a directional lamp produces its own cone of light, an omni-directional lamp must rely on the fixture and its trim to produce the cone and therefore has no candlepower rating. It is for this reason that the Inverse Square Law can't be used for omni-directional lamps. However, if a fixture manufacturer provides a CU table for a luminaire using a directional lamp, the Lumen Method can be used instead of the Inverse Square Law; both provide accurate results.

A CU table lists the amount of light from a luminaire which actually reaches the workplane. It is expressed as a percentage. For example, if a value from a CU table is .50, then 50% of the light the luminaire produces actually makes it to the workplane. The CU percentage is necessary to use the Lumen Method. Also, the CU table takes into account the reflectance levels in the room.

Reading a CU Table

In order to find a luminaire's efficiency for a room being designed, you must know the shape of the room, the colors used in the space, and the distance the lamps are from the workplane.

Lighting engineers have devised a way of defining the shape of the room and the distance of the lamp above the workplane as a whole number from 1 to 10. They call this number the RCR (room cavity ratio).

Finding the RCR

To arrive at the RCR you must plug the length and width of the room (in feet) and the distance (also in feet) into the formula below. As an example, let's use a room that is 15 feet in length, 10 feet in width, and where the lamp or luminaire will be 5 feet above the workplane. Plug the information into the formula and do the calculations. The first 5 in the formula is a constant; in other words, always a 5.

$$RCR = \frac{(5 \times Distance) \times (Length + Width)}{(Area)}$$

$$= \frac{(5 \times 5') \times (15' + 10')}{(15' \times 10')}$$

$$= \frac{25 \times 25}{150}$$

$$= \frac{625}{150}$$

$$= 4$$

Believe it or not, the engineers say this room has a RCR of 4. Always round to the nearest whole number.

Figure B.1 demonstrates how the RCR is used to determine the CU of a luminaire.

Using RCR and Reflectance to determine a luminaire's CU

Building on the example from the previous page, let's also assume that the example room has a white ceiling with a reflectance of 80%, and an average wall reflectance of 50%. The floor reflectance does not come into play as yet. Figure B.1 will use this new information as it explains how to derive the CU percentage from a CU table.

The table has been exploded for visual clarity.

① The first step is to decide where in the table to look. The table is broken into four major blocks (80%, 70%, 50%, 30%) which indicate the ceiling reflectance (CCR).

In our example, the ceiling is white which is usually considered 80%. The block labeled 80% has been pulled forward. The rest of your search will be confined to this block.

② The next step is to find the proper vertical column within the 80% block found in step 1. The block is broken into vertical columns by average wall reflectance (WCR).

In our example, the average wall reflectance is 50%. The vertical column labeled 50% has been pulled forward. The rest of your search will be confined to this column.

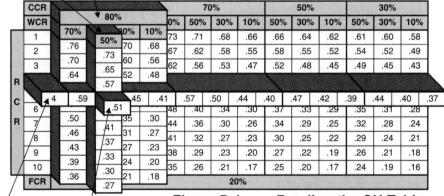

Figure B.1   Reading the CU Table

③ The RCR indicates the room shape and distance. There are always 10 horizontal RCR rows numbered from 1 to 10. You must now decide which row to look in.

In our example, the 10' x 15' room with a distance of 5' had a RCR of 4. Row 4 has been pulled forward. The rest of your search will be confined to this row.

④ You will find, where the vertical (WCR) column and the horizontal (RCR) row intersect, the CU percentage or efficiency of the luminaire (.51). In other words, 51% of the light generated by the luminaire actually reaches the workplane.

It is this CU percentage that is used in the Lumen Method Calculation Sheet explained in Chapter 4.

About the CU Tables in This Appendix

- All the CU tables included in this index are from the manufacturer of the fixture identified for each table.

- The fixture graphic for each table is generic and intended for rough planning purposes only. Always check the specifications for the intended fixture.

- Always use the lamp information, number of lamps, lumens, etc., included with the CU table that you are using.

  However, if for example, you were planning a surface mounted 4 foot fluorescent fixture like the ones in Tables **A** or **B**, and you wanted to use a higher quality lamp with better color temperature and CRI characteristics, proceed as follows:

  Find the CU for the fixture as usual, then substitute the lumens of the better lamp for the lumens of the lamp listed in the CU table. **Caution:** Only do this with lamps of the same type (i.e., F40T12 for F40T12, PAR 30 for PAR 30 Halogen, etc.).

- The double compact fluorescent luminaires in Tables **G** and **H** are equipped with one ballast for each lamp. If one switch is run to ballast A in each fixture while the other switch runs to ballast B, a quasi-dimming effect can be achieved similar to high-low beams in a cars' headlight. This is a low cost alternative to the more expensive dimmable ballasts.

TIP When the reflectances are not known, use:

CCR	80%
WCR	50%
FCR	20%

What to do When a CU Table Cannot be Found

- Sometimes the CU table will be difficult to find. I have included some commonly used luminaires that are dreadfully inefficient and some that I particularly like. The reason for this is so you can compare and draw your own conclusions.

- If you can't locate a CU table for a particular luminaire, yet a very similar one is listed in this section, use the CU from this book to approximate your fixture. It is far superior to guessing and is a common practice among lighting designers.

- Most of the compact fluorescent fixture manufacturers provide CU information in their general literature. However, finding a CU for a directional lamp used in a recessed can, for example, may be like finding a needle in a haystack.

- When planning to use a directional lamp luminaire and the CU table can't be found, either use one of the following tables (if it's close) or revert to the Inverse Square Law and use the cone of light, as described in Chapter 3, for spacing.

TABLE A

	CCR	80%				70%				50%			30%		
	WCR	70%	50%	30%	10%	70%	50%	30%	10%	50%	30%	10%	50%	30%	10%
	1	.76	.73	.70	.68	.73	.71	.68	.66	.66	.64	.62	.61	.60	.58
	2	.70	.65	.60	.56	.67	.62	.58	.55	.58	.55	.52	.54	.52	.49
	3	.64	.57	.52	.48	.62	.56	.53	.47	.52	.48	.45	.49	.45	.43
R	4	.59	.51	.45	.41	.57	.50	.44	.40	.47	.42	.39	.44	.40	.37
C	5	.54	.46	.39	.35	.52	.44	.39	.34	.42	.37	.33	.39	.35	.32
R	6	.50	.41	.35	.30	.48	.40	.34	.30	.37	.33	.29	.35	.31	.28
	7	.46	.37	.31	.27	.44	.36	.30	.26	.34	.29	.25	.32	.28	.24
	8	.43	.33	.27	.23	.41	.32	.27	.23	.30	.25	.22	.29	.24	.21
	9	.39	.30	.24	.20	.38	.29	.23	.20	.27	.22	.19	.26	.21	.18
	10	.36	.27	.21	.18	.35	.26	.21	.17	.25	.20	.17	.24	.19	.16
	FCR	20%													

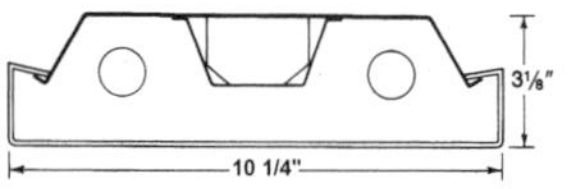

Manufacturer: Lithonia
Model: LB240A
Lamps: 2 ea 4' F40T12 34W
Lumens per Lamp: 2,650
Total Lumens: 5,300

Description:
This luminaire uses two 4' standard fluorescent T12 tubes, is ceiling mounted, and has a wraparound prismatic lens.

Comparison
In a 10' x 15' kitchen with a desired footcandle level of 40, 80% ceiling reflectance, 50% wall reflectance, and 20% floor reflectance: **3 luminaires**

Luminaires Per Square Foot Factor
3 luminaires ÷ 150 sq. ft. = **.02**

TABLE B

	CCR	80%				70%				50%			30%		
	WCR	70%	50%	30%	10%	70%	50%	30%	10%	50%	30%	10%	50%	30%	10%
	1	.74	.71	.68	.66	.72	.69	.67	.64	.65	.63	.61	.61	.60	.58
	2	.68	.63	.59	.55	.66	.61	.58	.54	.58	.55	.52	.55	.52	.50
	3	.63	.56	.51	.47	.61	.55	.50	.47	.52	.48	.45	.49	.46	.44
R	4	.58	.50	.45	.41	.56	.49	.44	.40	.47	.42	.39	.44	.41	.38
C	5	.53	.45	.39	.35	.51	.44	.39	.35	.42	.37	.34	.40	.36	.33
R	6	.49	.41	.35	.31	.47	.40	.34	.30	.38	.33	.30	.36	.32	.29
	7	.45	.37	.31	.27	.44	.36	.30	.27	.34	.29	.26	.33	.28	.25
	8	.42	.33	.27	.23	.40	.32	.27	.23	.31	.26	.23	.29	.25	.22
	9	.38	.29	.24	.20	.37	.29	.24	.20	.28	.23	.20	.26	.22	.19
	10	.36	.27	.21	.18	.35	.26	.21	.18	.25	.21	.17	.24	.20	.17
	FCR	20%													

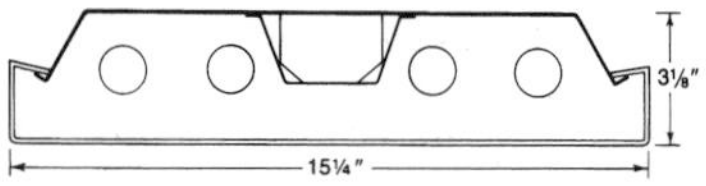

Manufacturer: Lithonia
Model: LB440A
Lamps: 4 ea 4' F40T12 34W
Lumens per Lamp: 2,650
Total Lumens: 10,600

Description:
This luminaire uses four 4' standard fluorescent T12 tubes, is ceiling mounted, and has a wraparound prismatic lens.

Comparison
In a 10' x 15' kitchen with a desired footcandle level of 40, 80% ceiling reflectance, 50% wall reflectance, and 20% floor reflectance: **1.5 luminaires**

Luminaires Per Square Foot Factor
1.5 luminaires ÷ 150 sq. ft. = **.01**

TABLE C

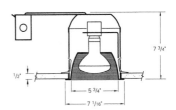

CCR		80%				70%			50%			30%		
WCR	70%	50%	30%	10%	70%	50%	30%	10%	50%	30%	10%	50%	30%	10%
1		.451	.442	.435		.441	.434	.427	.428	.421	.416	.411	.407	.403
2		.431	.415	.406		.423	.411	.401	.409	.401	.393	.401	.391	.385
3		.409	.394	.381		.404	.392	.379	.395	.387	.374	.386	.376	.368
4		.390	.375	.360		.383	.369	.357	.377	.364	.353	.370	.358	.349
5		.371	.354	.338		.374	.351	.338	.362	.348	.337	.356	.344	.33
6		.355	.338	.325		.353	.337	.323	.347	.333	.321	.341	.330	.319
7		.340	.322	.308		.338	.316	.306	.333	.316	.305	.328	.314	.303
8		.323	.304	.292		.319	.302	.291	.317	.301	.299	.313	.298	.288
9		.309	.288	.274		.305	.287	.274	.302	.285	.275	.299	.283	.273
10		.282	.260	.246		.278	.260	.246	.276	.257	.245	.271	.256	.245
FCR	20%													

R C R (row labels beside rows 4, 5, 6)

Manufacturer/Model:	Halo/H7-304
Trim:	Black Step Baffle
Lamps:	1 ea 75W R30 Flood
Lumens per Lamp:	900
Total Lumens:	900

Comparison

In a 10' x 15' kitchen with a desired footcandle level of 40, 80% ceiling reflectance, 50% wall reflectance, and 20% floor reflectance: **22.8 luminaires**

Luminaires Per Square Foot Factor

22.8 luminaires ÷ 150 sq. ft. = **.152**

Description:

This luminaire uses one 75W R30 flood lamp, is a recessed ceiling can, and is rated using a black step baffle trim. This is a very popular luminaire and has been included to show just how inefficient it is.

The black step baffle absorbs about half the light the lamp is producing!

TABLE D

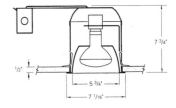

CCR		80%				70%			50%			30%		
WCR	70%	50%	30%	10%	70%	50%	30%	10%	50%	30%	10%	50%	30%	10%
1	.99	.96	.94	.92	.97	.94	.92	.90	.91	.89	.87	.87	.86	.85
2	.93	.88	.84	.81	.91	.87	.83	.80	.84	.81	.78	.81	.79	.77
3	.88	.81	.76	.72	.86	.80	.75	.72	.78	.74	.71	.75	.72	.69
4	.82	.75	.69	.65	.81	.74	.69	.65	.72	.67	.64	.70	.66	.63
5	.77	.69	.63	.59	.76	.68	.63	.59	.66	.62	.58	.65	.61	.58
6	.73	.64	.58	.54	.71	.63	.57	.53	.62	.57	.53	.60	.56	.53
7	.68	.59	.53	.49	.67	.59	.53	.49	.57	.52	.49	.56	.52	.48
8	.65	.55	.49	.45	.63	.55	.49	.45	.54	.48	.45	.53	.48	.45
9	.61	.51	.46	.42	.60	.51	.45	.42	.50	.45	.41	.49	.45	.41
10	.58	.48	.42	.39	.57	.48	.42	.39	.47	.42	.38	.46	.42	.38
FCR	20%													

R C R (row labels beside rows 4, 5, 6)

Manufacturer/Model:	Halo/H7-426
Trim:	Clear Alzak (Specular)
Lamps:	1 ea 75W R30 Flood
Lumens per Lamp:	900
Total Lumens:	900

Comparison

In a 10' x 15' kitchen with a desired footcandle level of 40, 80% ceiling reflectance, 50% wall reflectance, and 20% floor reflectance: **11.9 luminaires**

Luminaires Per Square Foot Factor

11.9 luminaires ÷ 150 sq. ft. = **.079**

Description:

This luminaire uses one 75W R30 flood lamp, is a recessed ceiling can, and is rated using a clear Alzak (Specular) trim. This luminaire, while better than the previous one, is still inefficient in comparison to the upcoming combinations.

By substituting the Alzak trim, the luminaire produces twice the illumination to the workplane when compared to one outfitted with a black step baffle.

CCR	80%				70%				50%			30%		
WCR	70%	50%	30%	10%	70%	50%	30%	10%	50%	30%	10%	50%	30%	10%
1		1.11	1.10	1.08		1.09	1.08	1.06	1.05	1.04	1.03	1.02	1.01	1.00
2		1.07	1.04	1.02		1.05	1.03	1.01	1.02	1.00	.98	.99	.98	.96
3		1.03	1.00	.97		1.01	.99	.97	.99	.97	.95	.97	.95	.94
R 4		.99	.96	.94		.99	.96	.93	.97	.94	.92	.95	.93	.91
C 5		.96	.92	.90		.95	.92	.89	.94	.91	.89	.92	.90	.88
R 6		.93	.90	.87		.93	.89	.87	.91	.89	.86	.90	.88	.86
7		.90	.87	.84		.90	.86	.84	.89	.86	.84	.88	.85	.83
8		.88	.84	.82		.87	.84	.81	.86	.83	.81	.86	.83	.81
9		.85	.81	.79		.84	.81	.79	.84	.81	.78	.83	.80	.78
10		.83	.79	.76		.82	.79	.76	.82	.78	.76	.81	.78	.76
FCR	20%													

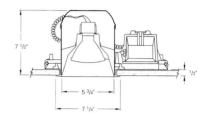

TABLE E

Manufacturer/Model: Halo/H7-426
Trim: Clear Alzak (Specular)
Lamps: 1 ea 75W PAR30 Flood
Lumens per Lamp: 1,030 (Halogen)
Total Lumens: 1,030

Comparison

In a 10' x 15' kitchen with a desired footcandle level of 40, 80% ceiling reflectance, 50% wall reflectance, and 20% floor reflectance: **7.8 luminaires**

Luminaires Per Square Foot Factor

7.8 luminaires ÷ 150 sq. ft. = **.052**

Description:

This luminaire uses one 75W PAR30 halogen flood lamp, is a recessed ceiling can, and is rated using a clear Alzak (Specular) trim. This luminaire is the most efficient of the three incandescent cans rated here.

This luminaire is a good choice for general lighting when short range budget is a constraint. Use one of the Epact rated halogen lamps for best efficiency and energy compliance.

CCR	80%				70%				50%			30%		
WCR	70%	50%	30%	10%	70%	50%	30%	10%	50%	30%	10%	50%	30%	10%
1	.77	.75	.74	.73	.76	.74	.73	.71	.71	.70	.69	.69	.68	.67
2	.74	.71	.68	.66	.72	.70	.67	.65	.67	.66	.64	.66	.64	.63
3	.70	.66	.63	.61	.69	.65	.63	.60	.64	.61	.59	.62	.60	.58
R 4	.67	.62	.59	.56	.66	.62	.59	.56	.60	.57	.55	.59	.57	.55
C 5	.64	.59	.55	.52	.63	.58	.54	.52	.57	.54	.51	.56	.53	.51
R 6	.61	.55	.51	.49	.60	.54	.51	.48	.53	.50	.48	.53	.50	.48
7	.57	.51	.48	.45	.57	.51	.47	.45	.50	.47	.45	.49	.46	.44
8	.55	.48	.44	.42	.54	.48	.44	.41	.47	.44	.41	.46	.43	.41
9	.52	.45	.41	.38	.51	.45	.41	.38	.44	.41	.38	.44	.40	.38
10	.49	.42	.38	.36	.48	.42	.38	.36	.41	.38	.36	.41	.38	.35
FCR	20%													

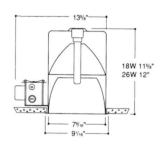

TABLE F

Manufacturer/Model: Prescolite/CFV26-892
Trim: Clear Alzak (Specular)
Lamps: 1 ea 26W Double Twin
Lumens per Lamp: 1,800
Total Lumens: 1,800

Comparison

In a 10' x 15' kitchen with a desired footcandle level of 40, 80% ceiling reflectance, 50% wall reflectance, and 20% floor reflectance: **7.2 luminaires**

Luminaires Per Square Foot Factor

7.2 luminaires ÷ 150 sq. ft. = **.048**

Description:

This luminaire uses one vertically positioned 26W Double Twin compact fluorescent lamp, is a recessed ceiling can, and is rated using a clear Alzak (Specular) trim.

Though this luminaire is far more efficient in the long run than the three incandescent cans shown previously, the lamp's vertical position is considered by more than a few designers as *ugly*. For an aesthetic improvement and greater efficiency, refer to the two following compact fluorescent luminaires.

TABLE G

CCR	80%				70%				50%			30%		
WCR	70%	50%	30%	10%	70%	50%	30%	10%	50%	30%	10%	50%	30%	10%
1	.70	.69	.67	.65	.69	.67	.66	.64	.65	.63	.62	.62	.61	.60
2	.67	.63	.61	.58	.65	.62	.60	.58	.60	.58	.56	.58	.57	.55
3	.63	.58	.55	.52	.61	.57	.54	.52	.56	.53	.51	.54	.52	.50
R 4	.59	.54	.50	.47	.58	.53	.50	.47	.52	.49	.46	.50	.48	.46
C 5	.55	.50	.45	.42	.54	.49	.45	.42	.48	.44	.42	.47	.44	.41
R 6	.52	.45	.41	.38	.51	.45	.41	.38	.44	.40	.38	.43	.40	.37
7	.48	.41	.37	.34	.47	.41	.37	.34	.40	.36	.34	.39	.36	.33
8	.45	.38	.33	.30	.44	.37	.33	.30	.37	.33	.30	.36	.32	.30
9	.41	.34	.30	.27	.41	.34	.30	.27	.33	.29	.27	.33	.29	.27
10	.38	.31	.27	.24	.38	.31	.27	.24	.30	.26	.24	.30	.26	.24
FCR	20%													

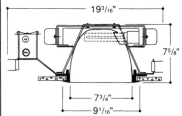

19³/₁₆" 7⁵/₈" 7³/₄" 9¹/₁₆"

Manufacturer/Model: Prescolite/CFR818-492
Trim: Clear Alzak (Specular)
Lamps: 2 ea 18W Double Twin
Lumens per Lamp: 1,250
Total Lumens: 2,500

Comparison

In a 10' x 15' kitchen with a desired footcandle level of 40, 80% ceiling reflectance, 50% wall reflectance, and 20% floor reflectance: **5.9 luminaires**

Luminaires Per Square Foot Factor
5.9 luminaires ÷ 150 sq. ft. = **.039**

Description:

This luminaire uses two horizontally positioned 18W Double Twin compact fluorescent lamps, is a recessed ceiling can, and is rated using a clear Alzak (Specular) trim. This is the most energy efficient and, over the long run, most cost effective luminaire design. The horizontal orientation of the lamps avoids the unsightliness of the previous luminaire while providing more light through the use of an extra lamp.

The only decision between this and the next unit is how many fixtures the designer wishes in the ceiling.

TABLE H

CCR	80%				70%				50%			30%		
WCR	70%	50%	30%	10%	70%	50%	30%	10%	50%	30%	10%	50%	30%	10%
1	.67	.65	.63	.62	.65	.64	.62	.61	.61	.60	.59	.59	.58	.57
2	.63	.60	.58	.55	.62	.59	.57	.55	.57	.55	.53	.55	.54	.52
3	.59	.55	.52	.49	.58	.54	.51	.49	.53	.50	.48	.51	.49	.48
R 4	.56	.51	.47	.45	.55	.50	.47	.44	.49	.46	.44	.48	.45	.43
C 5	.52	.47	.43	.40	.51	.46	.43	.40	.45	.42	.40	.44	.41	.39
R 6	.49	.43	.39	.36	.42	.43	.49	.36	.42	.38	.36	.41	.38	.36
7	.45	.39	.35	.32	.45	.39	.35	.32	.38	.34	.32	.37	.34	.32
8	.42	.36	.32	.29	.42	.35	.31	.29	.35	.31	.29	.34	.31	.29
9	.39	.33	.28	.25	.38	.32	.28	.25	.31	.28	.25	.31	.28	.25
10	.36	.29	.25	.23	.36	.29	.25	.23	.29	.25	.22	.28	.25	.22
FCR	20%													

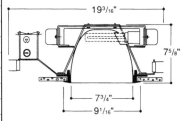

19³/₁₆" 7⁵/₈" 7³/₄" 9¹/₁₆"

Manufacturer/Model: Prescolite/CFR826-492
Trim: Clear Alzak (Specular)
Lamps: 2 ea 26W Double Twin
Lumens per Lamp: 1,800
Total Lumens: 3,600

Comparison

In a 10' x 15' kitchen with a desired footcandle level of 40, 80% ceiling reflectance, 50% wall reflectance, and 20% floor reflectance: **4.4 luminaires**

Luminaires Per Square Foot Factor
4.4 luminaires ÷ 150 sq. ft. = **.029**

Description:

This luminaire uses two horizontally positioned 26W Double Twin compact fluorescent lamps, is a recessed ceiling can, and is rated using a clear Alzak (Specular) trim. This is the most energy efficient and, over the long run, most cost effective luminaire design. The horizontal orientation of the lamps avoids the unsightliness of vertically oriented compact fluorescent lamps while providing more light.

The only decision between this and the previous unit is the number of fixtures desired.

GLOSSARY

Beam Angle

Any directional lamp emits light energy in the shape of a cone. As you might expect, the candlepower intensity is the greatest at the center of the cone and it diminishes the closer it gets to the edge of the cone; eventually, in theory, to zero. The usable portion of the cone is defined at the point where the candlepower falls to 50% of the candlepower at the center. Our eyes perceive this portion of the lamp's cone as one intensity of light even though, at its edges, the intensity has dropped to half. This portion of the total cone of light is termed the beam angle.

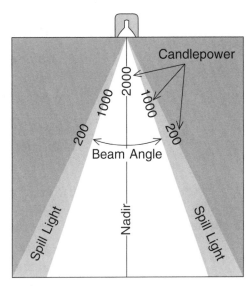

The Beam Angle is defined where Candlepower falls to 50%.

It is the beam angle we are concerned with when it comes to spacing one directional lamp to another.

The beam angle is found in the lamp manufacturers' lamp data chart.

See Chapter 3, *Spacing Principles*, for an in depth discussion on proper spacing techniques.

Candela

See candlepower.

Candlepower

The unit for measuring the quantity or intensity of light energy emitted by a directional lamp (i.e., narrow spot, spot, flood, wide flood, etc.).

Candlepower is expressed in candelas. Confusion is caused for some when one manufacturer lists a lamp's candlepower as "Center-Beam Candlepower" while another notes it as "Mean Candlepower" and yet another uses "Candela" as the heading for the same information in their lamp data chart. Any of these listings refer to the lamp candlepower and is considered to be the same.

Candlepower is used in the Inverse Square Law calculation.

Some texts indicate that 1 candela = 12.57 lumens; do not try to convert lumens to candelas using this formula. Results will be inaccurate.

See Chapter 1, *Lighting Concepts*, for more information on candlepower and Chapter 4, *Lighting Measurements*, for how to use candlepower in the Inverse Square Law.

Color Temperature

The color of the lamp itself as compared to the color of a black reference substance when heated to various temperatures Kelvin, and the effect the lamp color has on the color of an object being illuminated by it.

- Warm lamps range from: 2,700k to 3,000k
- Neutral lamps range from: 3,000k to 3,600k
- Cool lamps range from: 3,600k to 5,500k
- Fluorescent lamps are available in Cool, Neutral, & Warm.
- Halogen lamps are considered neutral.
- Incandescent lamps are considered warm.

A properly selected lamp will have appropriate color temperature and also provide a good CRI (Color Rendition Index).

See Chapter 2, *Color & Reflectance*, for more information on color temperature.

CRI

Color Rendition Index. A scale from 1 to 100 indicating a lamp's ability to render an object's color accurately. 100 is the best rating. For interior design work, only lamps over 80 should be used.

- Fluorescent lamps are available in 50, 60, 70, 80, & 90 CRI.

- Incandescent and incandescent halogen lamps are 100 CRI.

A properly selected lamp will have good color rendering properties and be of an appropriate color temperature.

See Chapter 2, *Color & Reflectance*, for more information on CRI.

CU Table

Coefficient of Utilization. The efficiency with which the luminaire (combination of fixture, fixture trim, and specific lamp) directs lumens to the workplane, expressed as a percentage. This CU percentage is listed in a table produced by the fixture manufacturer and is used in the Lumen Method to determine the number of fixtures required to achieve a given footcandle level in a space. The CU takes into account the shape, height, and color of the room. To select a number from a CU table, the ceiling reflectance, wall reflectance, floor reflectance, and the room cavity ratio (RCR) must be determined.

See Chapter 4, *Lighting Measurements*, for more information on using a CU table.

Distance

For down-lighting, it is the measurement from the lamp to the workplane.

Efficacy

The ratio of lumens produced by a lamp to the watts consumed, expressed as lumens per watt (LPW). The higher the lumens per watt, the more efficient the lamp.

Fixture

The housing or assembly that holds the lamp and/or trim.

Fluorescent Phosphors   The color of fluorescent lamps is created by mineral phosphors in powder form which coat the inside of the lamp tube. The chemical make-up of these phosphors determines the lamp's CRI, its color temperature, and how much light the lamp produces. There are four types of phosphor coatings:

Traditional halophosphors;   Are inexpensive coatings which usually provide the entire spectrum of light. But, there is a trade-off between color rendering and lumen output. Poor color rendering lamps such as "warm white" and "cool white" have high lumen output. Good color rendering lamps such as "warm white deluxe" and "cool white deluxe" have low lumen output.

Prime color or tri-phosphors;   Are very expensive coatings with good color rendering and high lumen output. Lamps of this type are produced under the trademark Ultralume.

Double-coat lamps;   Have a coat of halo-phosphor and a coat of tri-phosphor. Double-coat lamps which have a thick tri-phosphor coat are fairly expensive but have very good color rendering properties. They are known by the trademarks SPX, Designer 800 series, etc. Double-coat lamps with a thin tri-phosphor coat are much less expensive, but still have full light output and reasonably good color rendering. These lamps are known by the trademarks SP, SPEC, Designer, and others.

Rare earth phosphors;   Have a thin and thick coat of rare earth phosphors and are just becoming available. The CRI for these lamps will be 70, 80, and 90 and in a variety of color temperatures.

Footcandle (Fc)

The unit of measurement indicating the light present on a surface or workplane. Footcandle levels are determined by the IES (Illuminating Engineering Society) to provide an adequate amount of light for a visual task, whether it be walking through a space or studying a manuscript. Tasks requiring more visual acuity require a higher footcandle level.

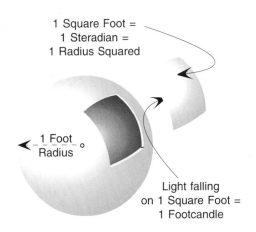

1 Square Foot =
1 Steradian =
1 Radius Squared

1 Foot
Radius

Light falling
on 1 Square Foot =
1 Footcandle

Note: 1 Footcandle is equal to the amount of light provided by an ordinary wax candle on a spherical surface with an area equal to one square foot, one foot away from the flame.

To convert Fc to Lux, use the formula:

Lux = Fc x 10.76

To convert Lux to Fc, use the formula:

Fc = Lux x .0929

If artwork is to be incorporated into the space, it must receive 5 times the amount of light as the surrounding space. This gives the art the perception of being highlighted or accented.

See Chapter 1, *Lighting Concepts*, for more information on footcandles and Chapter 4, *Lighting Measurements*, for details on how to determine footcandles for a room and how they are used in the Inverse Square Law and Lumen Method calculations.

Footlambert

The amount of light reflected off a surface. This reflected light adds to the overall illumination. The degree of reflectance is greatly dependent on the color in the space. White reflects approximately 80% of the light while black reflects only 4%.

See Chapter 2, *Color & Reflectance* for more information on this subject.

Inverse Square Law

For directional lamps (i.e., narrow spot, spot, flood, wide flood, etc.), a formula used to determine the relationship between the candlepower (Cp) of the lamp, the distance (D) the lamp is from the surface to be illuminated, and the footcandle (Fc) level produced on that surface. If any two of the three elements are known, the third can be determined.

$$\text{Candlepower} = D^2 \times Fc \quad or$$
$$\text{Footcandles} = Cp \div D^2 \quad or$$
$$\text{Distance} = \sqrt{Cp \div Fc}$$

Example: An island counter is 3 feet high in a kitchen with an 8 foot ceiling height. Recessed cans are to be used with a lamp rated at 1150 candlepower. The distance from the lamp to the counter surface is approximately 5 feet. By squaring the distance (D^2) between the counter and the lamp (5' x 5' = 25'), then dividing it into the lamps rated candlepower (1150), the footcandle level at the counter surface is found to be 46.

See Chapter 4, *Lighting Measurements*, for a more in depth discussion on using the Inverse Square Law.

Lamp

A man-made light source. Also known as a tube or bulb.

Light

The visible portion of the electromagnetic spectrum extending from 380 nanometers (ultraviolet end) to 770 nanometers (infrared end). White light is made up of three primary colors. The three primary colors of light are red, blue and green. The primary pigment colors are red, blue and yellow.

Line Voltage

120 volts. Lamps that operate at 120 volts are considered line voltage lamps.

Low Voltage

Lamps that operate at a lower voltage than line voltage are termed low voltage lamps. These lamps require a transformer to reduce line voltage usually to 12 or 24 volts.

Lumen

The unit of measurement used to indicate the quantity or intensity of any lamp. Think of it in terms of the lamp's raw power. Lumens are measured at the lamp.

Lumens are used in the Lumen Method calculation to determine the number of fixtures necessary and their spacing to maintain a given footcandle level as prescribed by the IES (Illuminating Engineering Society).

Some texts indicate that 1 candela = 12.57 lumens; do not try to convert lumens to candelas using this formula. Results will be inaccurate.

See Chapter 1, *Lighting Concepts*, for more information on lumens and Chapter 4, *Lighting Measurements*, for how to use lumens in the Lumen Method.

Lumen Method

A series of formulas used to determine the number of luminaires necessary to illuminate a space and the spacing needed to maintain a given footcandle level. A CU table from the manufacturer is a prerequisite in performing these calculations.

See Chapter 4, *Lighting Measurements*, for how to use the Lumen Method.

Luminaire   A complete lighting unit; an assemblage made up of the fixture, trim, and the lamp.

Lux   The metric unit of measurement indicating the light present on a surface or workplane. One might call lux the metric footcandle. It differs in that instead of using a sphere with a radius of one foot, it uses one meter. The amount of light falling on one square meter of the sphere is referred to as one lux.

Europeans manufacture many lighting products that are used in North America. Rather than learn the entire metric system of lighting measurements, do the calculations found in this book using footcandles, convert the results to Lux using the factor below, then select the fixture or lamp in its metric equivalent.

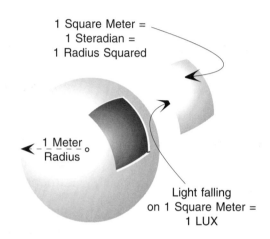

1 Square Meter =
1 Steradian =
1 Radius Squared

1 Meter Radius

Light falling on 1 Square Meter = 1 LUX

Note: 1 lux is equal to the amount of light provided by an ordinary wax candle on a spherical surface with an area equal to one square meter, one meter away from the flame.

To convert Lux to Fc, use the formula:

Fc = Lux x .0929

To convert Fc to Lux, use the formula:

Lux = Fc x 10.76

Nadir   Zero angle of light perpendicular to the lamp's face and bisecting the beam angle. If a lamp were placed in a typical recessed can in a level ceiling, nadir would be a vertical line perpendicular to the floor, ceiling, and lamp face.

Photometry

The measurement of quantities associated with light.

RCR

Room Cavity Ratio. A number indicating the room proportions calculated from the length, width and height. The result is a number (1 to 10) that is used to select a value from a CU table.

Spacing

The measurement between centers of luminaires.

Spacing should be at least equal to the beam diameter at the workplane to evenly maintain the footcandle level throughout a space. By decreasing this dimension the footcandles are increased; by increasing the spacing, the footcandles are reduced.

See Chapter 3, *Spacing Principles*, for more information on determining the spacing between fixtures.

Spacing Ratio

Often given by fixture manufacturer. Multiply the spacing ratio by the distance (in feet) from the fixture to the workplane.

Spill Light

Outside the beam angle is an area of "spill" light which extends from the beam angle out to a point in the lamps cone of light where the candlepower drops to 10% of the candlepower at the center of the cone.

Spill light is viable light, though not enough to consider for lamp spacing. It is enough to provide adequate illumination to wall cabinet fronts in a kitchen, for example. It is also useful as a "buffer zone" when ideal spacing can't be achieved due to existing ceiling joist locations, etc.

See Chapter 3, *Spacing Principles*, for an in depth discussion on proper spacing techniques.

Steradian

See footcandle and lux.

Watts

The amount of energy consumed by the lamp. Do not select a lamp based solely on wattage. This is a very common mistake. Wattage has nothing to do with the amount of light produced by a lamp.

A lamp should be chosen based on its candlepower or lumen rating which indicates the light energy intensity of the lamp. Only then should wattage be considered to find the most economical lamp among those lamps powerful enough to provide the proper footcandle level on the workplane.

Workplane

In any space there is an actual or implied height at which an activity takes place. At this height an imaginary plane which cuts through the entire room is assumed; the workplane. It is on this workplane that the footcandle measurement is taken. The IES (Illuminating Engineering Society) has determined appropriate footcandle levels for the workplane in every room of the home.

For a kitchen, the countertop is the workplane at 3 feet above the floor, the bath can be anywhere from 2 1/2 to 3 feet, a dining room or desk is 2 1/2 feet. When there is not a specific surface upon which an activity will take place, such as in a family or living room, a 2 1/2 foot workplane height is assumed. Whether you are calculating general or task illumination, the light level is determined in footcandles measured at the workplane height.

See Chapter 1, *Lighting Concepts*, for a more complete explanation of the workplane.

SOLUTIONS

Chapter 1

1. Task General

2. F

    General lighting provides illumination for moving about in the space, doing less visually demanding activities, and should be evenly distributed throughout the room. Task lighting is placed at specific locations where more visually demanding activities will take place. In a sewing room, for example, getting to stored materials or moving from the sewing machine to the ironing board would be a general lighting activity, while threading a needle would be a more demanding task activity requiring additional illumination.

3. b.) Workplane

    General and task lighting are always calculated for the workplane height.

4. 2 1/2 feet

    Even if there is no actual work surface, a virtual workplane is assumed at 2 1/2' above the floor. If one were reading while seated in a chair in a living room, the body position and the reading material would be at about the same height as if the person were seated at a desk. Using the floor to calculate light levels will result in providing too much illumination.

5. Lamp workplane

6. 3 1/2 feet

    8' ceiling ht., minus 1 1/2' pendant ht., minus 3' workplane height = 3 1/2'

7. Lumens

    Remember that all lamps produce a measurable raw quantity of light and can be measured in lumens.

8. b.) Directional

    Only directional lamps can have both candlepower and lumen measurements.

9. Lamp

    *For **any** lamp.*

10. Lamp

    For directional or focused lamps only. Those lamps having a beam angle.

11. Workplane

    The appropriate footcandle level on the workplane is the goal for task and general lighting. The footcandle is not a lamp measurement. It is a measurement of the amount of illumination on a given surface.

12. Lumen Method

    The Lumen Method uses the lamp's Lumen rating as part of the calculation in determining the number of lamps/fixtures necessary to provide a surface with a given footcandle level.

13. Inverse Square Law

    *Normally, you will be using either the Inverse Square Law **or** the Lumen Method to select lamps and/or fixtures.*

14. a.) Increase

    By focusing the lamps Lumen intensity into a concentrated beam angle, a candlepower measurement can be taken and the more tightly focused the beam angle, the higher the candlepower.

15. a.) Increase

    As the candlepower rises, the footcandles will rise at a given distance.

16. T

17. b.) Spacing lamps to provide even illumination.

    It is the width of the cone of light on the workplane determined by the lamp's beam angle that we are concerned with in fixture/lamp spacing.

18. F

    Watts have nothing to do with a lamp's ability to produce light. Watts do tell of a lamps efficiency, however. The more Lumens created per watt of energy burned, the more efficient the lamp.

19. The lamp manufacturers' Lamp Data Chart or Specification Sheet.

20. T

    Candlepower is expressed in candelas much like length is expressed in inches. You will often find that one manufacturer will list candlepower, one candelas, one mean candlepower, one center candlepower, all intended to convey the same information. It is confusing, but, they are all referring to the same candlepower of the lamp.

Chapter 2

1. c.) Render the colors of an object accurately

2. T

3. c.) 80 CRI

    Below 80 CRI will make the color of materials used in the space appear wrong. I can't think of a situation where a designed interior space would benefit from a lamp that would cause the colors of objects used in the space to appear incorrect regardless of the price of the lamp.

4. e.) All of the above.

5. F

    Remember that all incandescent lamps will have a CRI over 98 which is considered perfect. Fluorescent lamps, however, are available from 50 to 90 CRI. Care should be taken to select only those over 80 CRI for designed interiors.

6. T

    A halogen lamp is an incandescent lamp; a special type of incandescent lamp that uses halogen gas. It is not a distinct technology like fluorescent.

7. c.) "Warm" which intensifies "warm" colors, causes neutral colors to appear pink, and negates "cool" colors.

8. T

    Most color schemes include both warm and cool colors. Using neutral color temperature lamps is the logical choice to avoid affecting the colors of objects used in the room. Selecting lamps on the "warm" side of neutral allows people in the room (all people are inherently warm objects) to appear more "alive" while not adversely affecting the color scheme.

9. b.) 2900k - 3200k

    Just a hint … These lamps are on the warm side of neutral.

    To match a fluorescent lamp to halogen, try 3,500k fluorescents.

10. T

    Most incandescents will range in color temperature from 2700k - 3000k. Incandescent halogen lamps, however, vary in that they are in the 2900k - 3200k color temperature range.

11. T

12. F

    Lamps should be selected considering both CRI and color temperature. It is almost impossible to go wrong with a lamp that is 80+ CRI and in the 2900k - 3600k range.

13. F

    It is perfectly acceptable to mix Incandescent and fluorescent so long as all lamps appear to be the same color temperature and over 80 CRI.

    3,500k fluorescent and halogen work very well together.

14. d.) All of the above.

15. T

    The one exception is that red can be considered as either warm or cool.

16. __20__ %

    In looking at the reflectance table in Chapter 2, the closest material is probably the dark walnut which has a reflectance of 15% - 20%. 20% reflectance is the best choice because the rich mahogany stained cherry is still a little lighter than dark walnut. We are just trying to be in the ball park here.

17. Refer to the reflectance table in Chapter 2 to approximate the reflectance of materials used in question 17.

Ceiling Reflectance   __80__ %
    Use white at 80%.

Cabinetry   *.50 x* __.40__ *=*   __20__ %
Average Maple (60%) & Dark Oak (20%) to get 40%.

Wall Covering   *.25 x* __.35__   *=*   __09__ %
Use olive green at 35%.

Openings   *.25 x* __.04__   *=*   __01__ %
    Average zero reflectance for openings to other rooms (0%) & 8% for glass windows to get 4%.

Wall Reflectance   __30__ %
    Add the reflectance percentages for the three wall components to determine the combined wall reflectance:
    20% + 09% + 01% = 30%

Floor Reflectance   __70__ %
    Use Light Cream at 70% for beige.

Overall Reflectance   __60__ %
    $$\frac{80\% + 30\% + 70\%}{3}$$
    Average the ceiling, wall, & floor reflectance percentages (3) to determine the overall room reflectance.

18. __30__ %

    The rust counter color is somewhere between yellow ocher and orange. Since both have the same reflectance (25% - 35%), use 30%.

19. b.) Medium reflectance

    Choosing a "middle" ground for reflectance will probably be the safest bet if the materials are not selected when the lighting plan is executed.

20. T

    See Chapter 4, Lighting Measurements, to see how reflectance plays a large part in lamp selection.

Chapter 3

1. d.) All of the above.

2. T

3. a.) 1/2 cones.

4. d.) Two 1/2 cones.

5. b.) There will be a gap of light resulting in a dark area.

6. c.) 48 inches - 72 inches.

7. __0__ " to __18__ "

8. __6__ "

9. Maximum spacing.

10 degrees	__10__ "
29 degrees	__31__ "
53 degrees	__60__ "

10. Spacing with 6" intersect.

10 degrees	__9__ "
29 degrees	__28__ "
53 degrees	__54__ "

11. First fixture off the wall.

10 degrees	*__13__ "
29 degrees	__24__ "
53 degrees	__38__ "

In this case the cone of light resting on the workplane is 10 inches. Half the width of the cone (5 inches) plus the 8 inches constant will result in a spacing of 13 inches from the wall to the first lamp. However, the cone of light still breaks the face of the wall cabinetry. This should be one clear indicator that the beam angle is too narrow for a general lighting application, not to mention the Swiss cheese effect the 9 inch spacing will produce!

Use the spacing table, Figure 3.15, to find the following:

12. __55__ °

    In the 4.5' row (5 foot distance minus the 6 inch intersect), travel across to 56". Now travel up the column to find 55°.

13. __45__ °

    In the 5.5' row (6 foot distance minus the 6 inch intersect), travel across to 55". Now travel up the column to find 45°.

14. __40__ °

    In the 6.5' row (7 foot distance minus the 6 inch intersect), travel across to 57". Now travel up the column to find 40°.

    Note: for questions 12 through 14, to maintain spacing between lamps as the distance increases, the beam angle must decrease. Again think of cones, the further a cone of light must travel to the workplane, the wider it becomes.

15.   __30__ °

   In the 5' distance row, travel across to find the 32" column and follow it up to find the 30° beam angle.

16.   __22.5__ °

   In the 5' distance row, travel across to find 21" and 27". The 24 inch target is halfway between the two. In looking at the beam angle for both 21" and 27", we find 20° and 25° respectively. A 24 inch diameter circle will be produced by the angle halfway between 20° and 25°; 22.5°. Questions 15 and 16 look for the diameter of the cone as it rests on the workplane this has nothing to do with an intersect height above the workplane.

17.   __29__ "

   Once the 32" is found in question 15, simply read one row up (4.5' distance) to find the spacing at a 6 inch intersect.

18.   __21.5__ "

   In question 16 we found the 21" and 27" spacing with no intersect at a 5 foot distance. Moving up 6 inches to the 4.5' distance row for each, find 19" and 24" respectively. The spacing will be halfway between at 21.5 inches.

19.   __34__ "

   Travel across the beam angle row at the top to the 40° column. Travel down this column to the 6' row to find the width of the cone at 52". Half of 52" will be half the cone at 26 inches. Adding one half cone (26 inches) to the constant for wall cabinets (8 inches) will yield 34 inches.

20.   The fixture and trim redirect the light from an omni-directional lamp into a cone of light. The lamp cannot do it on its own. Therefore, there is no measurable beam angle. In Chapter 4, the Lumen Method provides a way to determine fixture spacing for omni-directional luminaires. Think of this spacing interval as the width of the cone as it rests upon the workplane. It is then a simple matter to divide the half cones into the length and width of the room as with directional lamping.

Chapter 4

1. T

2. Bath general   30 Fc

    Kitchen general   30 Fc

    Kitchen task   75 Fc

3. c.)   71 Fc

    The base footcandle level for general lighting in a bath is 30 Fc. A cumulative adjustment must be made for occupant age (over 55), average room reflectance ("dark"), and counter color ("dark"). The respective adjustment factors for each are 1.33, 1.33, and 1.33. The cumulative answer is:
    30 x 1.33 x 1.33 x 1.33 = 71 Fc.

4. c.)   100 Fc

    The base footcandle level for task lighting in a kitchen is 75 Fc. After adjusting for occupant age (75 x 1.33 = 100), we assume a "medium" reflectance for the average room and the counter color. These last two both have an adjustment factor of 1, so the cumulative adjustment will be:
    75 x 1.33 x 1 x 1 = 100 Fc.

5. b.)   5

6. b.)   directional lamps

    The Inverse Square Law deals with candlepower. Only lamps with a beam angle have candlepower.

7. c.)   2500 Cp

    The formula for candlepower is:

    $$Cp = Fc \qquad x \qquad D^2$$
    $$= 100 \qquad x \qquad 5^2$$
    $$= 100 \qquad x \qquad 25$$
    $$= 2500 \ Cp$$

    Don't forget to convert the 60 inches distance to 5 feet.

8. 886 Cp

    In the 2.25' (27 inch) row, travel across to the 75 Fc column to find 380 Cp, then continue across to the 100 Fc column to find 506 Cp. Add the two together to arrive at the Cp for the lamp.

9. b.)   result in a lower Fc level as the distance to the lamp increases across the vault.

10. 39"

    $$D = \sqrt{Cp \div Fc}$$
    $$= \sqrt{1400 \div 133}$$
    $$= \sqrt{10.526}$$
    $$= 3.24' \ or \ 39"$$

11. 56 Fc

    $$Fc = Cp \qquad \div \qquad D^2$$
    $$= 900 \qquad \div \qquad 4^2$$
    $$= 900 \qquad \div \qquad 16$$
    $$= 56 \ Fc$$

    Did you remember to convert the 48" distance to 4'?

12. T

    See figure 4.5

13. c.) Beam angle and candlepower

14. T

    However, only if the manufacturer has provided a CU table!

15. T

    The IES also publishes generic CU tables.

16. T

17. F

    The Lumen Method Worksheet will provide the number of luminaires and the spacing to maintain the desired Fc level.

18. See the Lumen Method Sheet on the next page.

19. .047 fixtures per Sq. Ft.

    See how this compares with the factor for this luminaire in Appendix B. Remember this kitchen had dark counters which increased the footcandle level from 40 to 53. So many things can affect the outcome!

Lumen Method Calculation Sheet

Project Name: _CU Table G   ---Kitchen---_
Fixture Manufacturer: _Prescolite_
Model Number: _CFR818-492_
Room Length: ___12'___ ft.   Room Width: ___11'___ ft.
Lamp Type: _18W DoubleTwin Compact Fluorescent_
Color Temperature: _3,000k_   CRI: _82_
Lamps per Fixture: ___2___   Lumens per Lamp: _1,250_
Total Fixture Lumens: _2,500_
Desired Footcandle Level: _53 Fc_

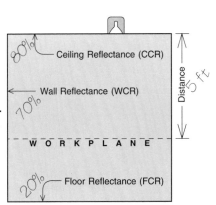

Step 1: Determine RCR (Room Cavity Ratio):

$$\text{RCR} = \frac{(5 \times \text{Distance in Feet}) \times (\text{Room Length} + \text{Room Width})}{(\text{Area in Square Feet})}$$

(5   12   11')

round to the nearest whole number... 4

$$= \frac{(\ \ 25'\ \ ) \times (\ \ 23'\ \ )}{(\ 132\ sq.\ ft.\ )}$$

$$= \frac{(\ \ 575\ \ )}{(\ \ 132\ \ )} \qquad\qquad \text{RCR} = \underline{\ 4.4\ }$$

Step 2: CCR ___.80___ ~ *use 80% if ceiling reflectance is unknown.*
Step 3: WCR ___.70___ ~ *use 50% if wall reflectance is unknown.*
Step 4: FCR ___.20___ ~ *use 20% if floor reflectance is unknown.*
Step 5: **CU**: ___.59___ ~ *use the info from steps 1-4 to obtain CU from a manufacturers' table.*
Step 6: LLF: ___.75___ ~ *use 75% as a rule of thumb. (Light Loss Factor)*
Step 7: Number of Fixtures:

$$= \frac{(\text{Footcandle Level}) \times (\text{Area in Square Feet})}{(\text{Total Fixture Lumens}) \times (\textbf{CU}) \times (\text{LLF})}$$

round to the nearest whole fixture... 6

$$= \frac{(\ \ 53\ Fc\ \ ) \times (132\ sq.\ ft.)}{(\ 2,500\ ) \times (\ .59\ CU\ ) \times (\ .75\ LLF\ )}$$

$$= \frac{(\ 6,996\ )}{(\ 1,106\ )} \qquad \text{Number of Fixtures} = \underline{\ 6.3\ }$$

Step 8: Fixture Spacing:

$$= \sqrt{\frac{(\text{Total Fixture Lumens}) \times (\textbf{CU}) \times (\text{LLF})}{(\text{Footcandle Level})}}$$

$$= \sqrt{\frac{(\ 2,500\ ) \times (\ .59\ CU\ ) \times (\ .75\ LLF\ )}{(\ 53\ Fc\ )}}$$

or 55'

$$= \sqrt{\frac{(\ 1,106\ )}{(\ 53\ Fc\ )}} \qquad \text{Fixture Spacing} = \underline{\ 4.57\ } \text{ ft.}$$

REFERENCE LIST

David K. Ballast, AIA, **Interior Design Reference Manual**, Belmont, CA: Professional Publications, Inc., 1992.

Edward Effron, **Lighting**, Boston: Little, Brown & Co., 1986.

Illuminating Engineering Society, **Lighting Handbook 8th Edition,** New York, NY, Illuminating Engineering Society, 1993, Reprinted 1995.

Illuminating Engineering Society, **IES Lighting Ready Reference,** New York, NY, Illuminating Engineering Society, 1989.

National Kitchen & Bath Association, **Kitchen and Bathroom Industry Technical Manuals #2,** Hackettstown, NJ, National Kitchen & Bath Association, 1996 and 1997.

Phillips Lighting Company, **Lighting Handbook, P-2260,** Somerset, NJ, Phillips Lighting Company, 1984.

RESOURCES

Ardee
PO Box 370375, Miami, FL 33137
(305) 531-7978

Capri
6430 E. Slauson Avenue, Los Angeles, CA 90040
(213) 726-1800

CSL
25070 Avenue Tibbetts, Valencia, CA 91355
(805) 257-4155

GE
Nela Park, Cleveland, OH 44112
(216) 266-2121

Halo
400 Busse Road, Elk Grove Village, IL 60007
(708) 956-1537

Hera
6659 Peachtree Ind. Blvd. - Suite M, Norcross, GA 30092
(770) 409-8558

Juno
2001 S. Mt. Prospect Road, Des Plaines, IL 60017-5065
(708) 827-9880

Lightolier
346 Claremont Avenue, Jersey City, NJ 07305
(212) 349-3100

Lucifer
414 Live Oak Street, San Antonio, TX 78202
(210) 227-7329

Kurt Versen
10 Charles Street, Westwood, NJ 07675
(201) 664-8200

Osram-Sylvania
100 Endicott Street, Danvers, MA 01923
(800) 255-5042

Phillips
200 Franklin Square Drive, Somerset, NJ 08875-6800
(800) 631-1259

Prescolite
1251 Doolittle Drive, San Leandro, CA 94577
(510) 562-3500

INDEX

LIGHTING SOFTWARE

Lighting Design Software

Doing the necessary calculations to specify proper lighting; color, spacing, footcandles, lamp candlepower, and lumens (even with the shortcuts in this book) can become repetitive and tedious. LightCalc was developed to speed the process for designers of residential interiors. Using the information the designer has readily available (ceiling height, room width and length, counter height, etc.) LightCalc instantly and accurately calculates the necessary footcandles, the lamp candlepower to provide it and then dimensions the correct spacing. LightCalc is an intuitive Windows based lighting design and presentation tool.

LightCalc will:

- **determine the footcandle level necessary for task, general, and art lighting.**

- **adjust the footcandle level for the colors used in the room.**

- **calculate the proper lamp candlepower for any lamp height.**

- **dimension the proper spacing needed.**

- **determine the number of fixtures needed using the lumen method.**

- **even suggest a ceiling layout for general lighting.**

- **all without remembering one single formula.**

In addition, LightCalc visually represents what the lighting is doing so the designer can **see** the results.

Footcandle

As you have read in this book, all lighting requires that you start with the footcandle level. Once the designer clicks on a room (kitchen, bath, office, etc.) LightCalc automatically calculates the appropriate footcandle level for general, task and artwork in the selected room. LightCalc also allows the designer to adjust for client age and the color palette.

Color

Color does affect the amount of lighting required in a room. Simply click a color for the ceiling, walls, and floor. LightCalc adjusts the footcandle level accordingly!

Inverse Square Law

Probably the most important set of formulae when it comes to directional lighting (i.e., flood, spot, PAR, MR16, etc.) is the Inverse Square Law. LightCalc makes its use a snap.

The designer simply enters the room and counter heights and the program instantly provides the candlepower of the lamp to use. Enter the beam angle of the lamp and LightCalc creates a section view of the cone of light and the correct spacing.

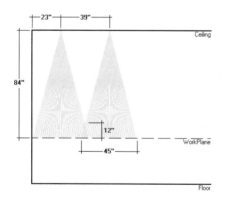

Change the ceiling height and the cones of light are resized and dimensioned.

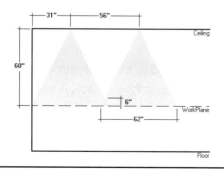

Click on *Kitchen* and the section view depicts the wall and base cabinetry with the cones shifted and re-dimensioned to prevent scalloping on the face of the wall cabinets.

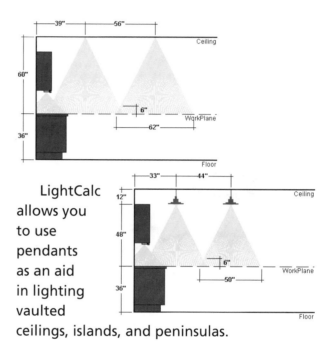

LightCalc allows you to use pendants as an aid in lighting vaulted ceilings, islands, and peninsulas.

Lumen Method

For fluorescent and compact fluorescent lamps, LightCalc will determine the number of lamps needed and their spacing using the Lumen Method (a cumbersome trial and error method by hand). The program will even suggest a ceiling layout so you can get a fast start on your reflected ceiling plan.

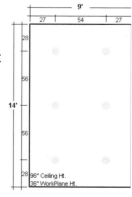

Lux to Footcandle Conversion

This allows you to calculate European products (Hafele, Hera, etc.) within LightCalc.

On-Line Help

LightCalc comes complete with an on-line help system that takes you, step by step, through the use of the program and your lighting plan. Included with the Help file are:

- **a glossary of lighting terms defined in easy to understand language.**

- **a convenient listing of fluorescent and incandescent lamps which can be used with Inverse Square Law calculations.**

- **fixture efficiency tables (CU) for use with the Lumen Method.**

ENVIRO-SYSTEMS has worked with Michael De Luca, CKD, ASID to provide you with a tool that works the way you do, *visually*, while saving you the one thing you need most, *time*.

Order LightCalc Today!!!

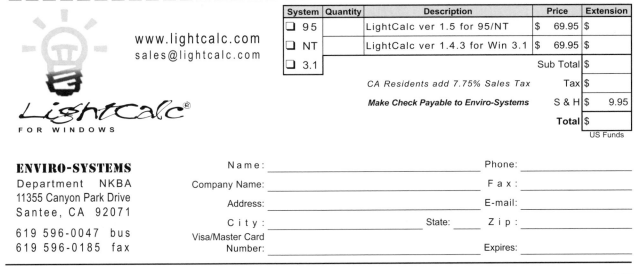

www.lightcalc.com
sales@lightcalc.com

LightCalc®
FOR WINDOWS

System	Quantity	Description	Price	Extension
❏ 95		LightCalc ver 1.5 for 95/NT	$ 69.95	$
❏ NT		LightCalc ver 1.4.3 for Win 3.1	$ 69.95	$
❏ 3.1			Sub Total	$
		CA Residents add 7.75% Sales Tax	Tax	$
		Make Check Payable to Enviro-Systems	S & H	$ 9.95
			Total	$

US Funds

ENVIRO-SYSTEMS
Department NKBA
11355 Canyon Park Drive
Santee, CA 92071

619 596-0047 bus
619 596-0185 fax

Name: _____

Company Name: _____

Address: _____

City: _____ State: _____ Zip: _____

Visa/Master Card
Number: _____

Phone: _____

Fax: _____

E-mail: _____

Expires: _____

NOTES

NOTES